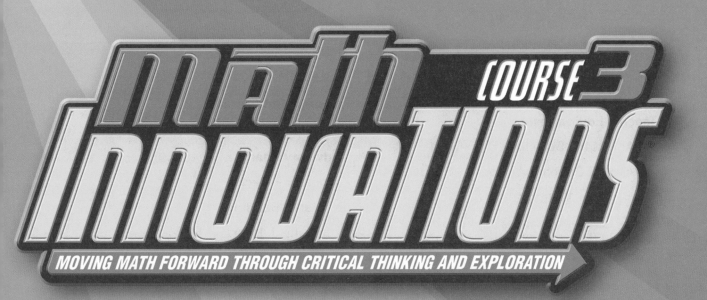

Delving into Data

Focusing on Representing, Interpreting and Analyzing Data

M. Katherine Gavin

Linda Jensen Sheffield

Suzanne H. Chapin

Kendall Hunt
publishing company

ACKNOWLEDGMENTS

Math Innovations Writing Team

Authors

M. Katherine Gavin

Linda Jensen Sheffield

Suzanne H. Chapin

Project Manager

Janice M. Vuolo

Teacher Edition Team

Ann Marie Spinelli

Alice J. Gabbard

Jacob J. Whitmore

Writing Assistants

Kathy Dorkin

Jane Paulin

Mathematics Editor

Kathleen G. Snook

Assessment Specialist

Nancy Anderson

Advisory Board

Jerry P. Becker

Janet Beissinger

Diane J. Briars

Ann Lawrence

Ira J. Papick

Cover photo of girl with clipboard by TSI Graphics. Unless otherwise noted, all images on cover and interior used under license by ShutterStock, Inc. Page 26 photo courtesy of M. Katherine Gavin. Page 97 photo © Larry W. Smith/epa/Corbis

Kendall Hunt
publishing company

www.kendallhunt.com
Send all inquiries to:
4050 Westmark Drive
Dubuque, IA 52004-1840
1-800-542-6657

Printed in the United States of America
4 5 6 7 8 9 10   14 13 12

Production Date: 11/28/12
Printed by: OneTouchPoint - CCI
           Hartland, Wisconsin
           United States of America
           Batch number: 42674204

Delving into Data:
Focusing on Representing, Interpreting and Analyzing Data

Table of Contents

UNIT GOALS

Delving into Data: Focusing on Representing, Interpreting and Analyzing Data

After studying this unit, you should be able to:

- Describe the distribution of a data set using maximum and minimum values, range, gaps and clusters;
- Determine appropriate measure of center to use with a given data set (mean, median and/or mode);
- Compare two or more data sets using appropriate tools and methods;
- Create a stem-and-leaf plot;
- Create a five-number summary and box-and-whisker plot;
- Create a scatter plot, look for a possible correlation and find a line of best fit, if appropriate;
- Interpret a variety of graphs and data displays (bar graphs, line plots, stem-and-leaf plots, box-and-whisker plots, scatter plots and lines of best fit);
- Determine appropriate graphs and data displays to use with a given data set.

Dear Student Mathematician,

In *Delving into Data,* you will learn how researchers conduct research studies and how they organize, analyze and interpret the data they gather. You will see how statisticians are a vital component in the research process in describing and analyzing data. You will revisit the mean, median and mode as measures of center and you will make and interpret different types of graphs, such as line plots, bar graphs, histograms, line graphs and circle graphs.

You will learn about another graph called a box-and-whisker plot, learn about correlation between two variables and learn how to determine a line of best fit. At this stage in your mathematical career, you are ready to look at a more complete picture of data analysis. You will become a data detective, carefully analyzing the data to see what story it is telling. You will do this by looking at the entire data set and seeing how its values are distributed, where there are clusters or gaps, if there is a minimum or maximum and how measures of center can help you uncover the story that the data are telling. You will also become knowledgeable about which data displays are most appropriate for telling the story you uncover.

As you complete this unit, you will see how data-driven decisions are used in a variety of fields. We hope you enjoy the activities and that you become better mathematicians through solving interesting problems related to data.

Mathematically Yours,
The Authors

M. Katherine Gavin   Linda Sheffield   Suzanne H. Chapin

SECTION 1

Data Snooping: Using Measures of Center

Welcome to the world of research! In this unit you will be a researcher who gathers, represents, analyzes and interprets data. To analyze data, researchers use statistics. You have heard and probably even used the term *statistics* before. For example, you may have seen an ad on TV claiming that 8 out of 10 kids prefer a certain chocolate drink mix, or 4 out of 5 dentists prefer a particular toothpaste. You may have read the statistics reported for players in a Red Sox game in the newspaper. Statistics themselves are numerical values used to describe or summarize a much larger set of values. One baseball statistic is how many hits a player makes compared to how many times he is at bat. This is known as a batting average.

Throughout this unit, you will learn how researchers obtain these numerical values and how they report them to the public. The statistics we will explore are called descriptive statistics since they describe a set of data in more detail. You will have an opportunity to gather, analyze, display and describe data using these statistics to help others make good decisions about situations they encounter and questions they are trying to answer. In this first section, you will revisit measures of center (mean, median and mode) and use them along with the distribution of the data to help tell the story that the data are showing.

LESSON 1.1

What's the Story?

Start It Off

MATHEMATICALLY SPEAKING

▶ data
▶ statistics
▶ descriptive statistics
▶ data analysis

With a partner, construct a concept map with DATA ANALYSIS written in the middle. Together, brainstorm what other words or ideas are related to data analysis. DESCRIPTIVE STATISTICS should be a category in your concept map. You may want to look up this term in an online mathematics dictionary. Share your map with the class and discuss what you know about data analysis and statistics.

A Balancing Act

Good balance is important for people throughout their lives. Balance helps us walk, dance, bike, hike, skateboard and perform most other physical activities. To test balance, doctors may time how long patients can balance on one foot. Students at Rockledge Middle School wanted to find out how long an average eighth-grader can balance on one foot. They conducted an experiment in their class. Below is a line plot showing the information they found.

MATHEMATICALLY SPEAKING

▶ line plot

▶ range

Number of Seconds Balancing on One Foot

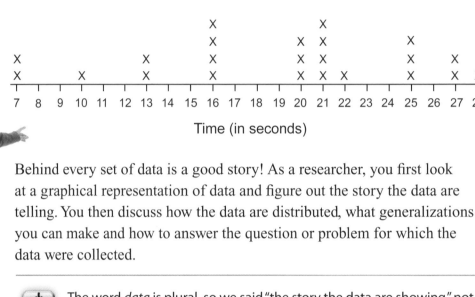

Time (in seconds)

Behind every set of data is a good story! As a researcher, you first look at a graphical representation of data and figure out the story the data are telling. You then discuss how the data are distributed, what generalizations you can make and how to answer the question or problem for which the data were collected.

NOTE The word *data* is plural, so we said "the story the data are showing," not "the story the data is showing." The singular of *data* is *datum* and refers to just one piece of data.

Analyze the data display by answering the following questions.

1. How many students balanced for 25 seconds? How did you find this number?

2. How many students were in the class? How did you find this number?

3. What is the minimum amount of time that a student could balance? What is the maximum amount of time?

The range of a data set is the difference between the maximum value and the minimum value. It is useful to describe how spread out the values of the data set are.

4. What is the range of this data set? Would you consider this to be a large spread of data for this experiment or would you consider the data to be fairly consistent for this group of middle school students? Explain.

When describing the distribution of the data, you should discuss range, along with gaps and clusters. Our common use of these vocabulary terms is also how they are used when we describe a data set statistically. Gaps are intervals of numbers for which there are no data values, and clusters are intervals where several data values are grouped closely together.

5. Describe the distribution of the data set for Rockledge Middle School.

6. What might the students at Rockledge Middle School decide is the "typical" number of seconds an eighth-grader can balance on one foot? Explain your answer.

7. Carlos thought a "typical" number of seconds could be 19 since that was the mean. Ana found the median and thought that was a better "typical" number. (The median is the number in the middle when a data set is arranged in order from least to greatest. It divides the data set into two equal halves with as many data points above it as below it.) Talk to your partner.

   a) What is the median of this data set?

   b) How does a median differ from a mean in what each tells you about the data?

   c) Which do you think describes this data set best? Explain.

 **Hint**
See page 121

8. Jon said he looked for the mode and found two of them. (When a data set has two different values that appear most frequently in the set, we describe the set as bimodal.)

   a) Which data values was he talking about?

   b) Do you consider either of these modes to be a typical value for the data set? Why or why not?

Carlos, Ana and Jon all used numerical values to describe an overall "average" of a set of data. We call these values—the mean, median and mode—measures of center, or measures of central tendency. They are used to describe a number that comes close to the center or a "typical" value of the data set. The three most common measures of central tendency are the mean, median and mode.

9. Sierra has just joined the class and wants to test her balance. Which measure of central tendency would you use to predict how long she will be able to balance on one foot? Why?

10. What other considerations should you take into account beyond the numbers to help you tell the story of these data?

Conduct the same experiment in your class to determine the typical number of seconds an eighth-grader can balance on one foot. Work in groups of three. One person will balance on one foot, one person will watch to determine when balance has been lost and one person will be the timer. Repeat the process so each person in the group has a chance to try balancing. Use the directions below to do the experiment.

Balancer: Wearing flat shoes, stand straight with your arms folded across your chest. Raise one leg, bending the knee about 45 degrees, close your eyes and balance.

Watcher: Say "GO" when the balancer is in the balance position. Say "STOP" immediately if the balancer uncrosses his or her arms, tilts sideways more than 45 degrees, moves the balance leg or touches the raised leg to the floor.

Timer: Start a stopwatch when the watcher says "GO" and stop the stopwatch when the watcher says "STOP." Record the time.

11. Gather data from everyone in the class. Create and display a line plot of the class data.

12. Describe the distribution of the data. Include the range, gaps and clusters. What does the distribution tell you about your class data?

13. Using a measure of center, describe a "typical" number of seconds a person in your class might balance. How did you find this number?

14. Compare your class's results to those found by students at Rockledge Middle School. How does the distribution of data compare? Would you now change your "typical" number of seconds that an eighth-grader can balance on one foot? Explain.

15. Look at the line plots for both sets of data. You used this information to describe a "typical" number of seconds for an eighth-grader to balance on one foot. What are some other questions related to this problem that you can *not* answer by examining only these line plots? What would you have to do to answer these new questions?

Believe It or Not!

The world record for balancing on one foot is 76 hours and 40 minutes by Arulanantham Suresh Joachim (Sri Lanka) at Vihara Maha Devi Park Open Air Stadium, Sri Lanka, from May 22–25, 1997! Even with his eyes open and hands by his sides, this is pretty amazing.

Wrap It Up

Discuss with your partner how the range, gaps, clusters, mean, median and mode are helpful in "telling the story" about a data set. Share your ideas with the class.

MATHEMATICALLY SPEAKING

- ▶ bimodal
- ▶ clusters
- ▶ data
- ▶ data analysis
- ▶ descriptive statistics
- ▶ distribution of data
- ▶ gaps
- ▶ line plot
- ▶ mean
- ▶ measures of center (or of central tendency)
- ▶ median
- ▶ mode
- ▶ range
- ▶ statistics

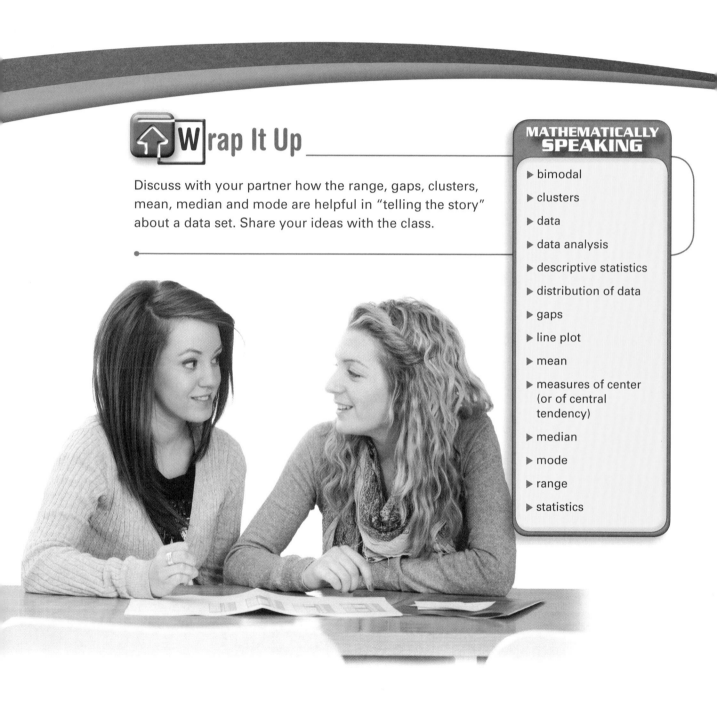

 **Write About It**

1. Refine the concept map of DATA ANALYSIS you created in the Start It Off. Make sure to include each of the Mathematically Speaking terms. You may also add or delete other terms or phrases

2. **a)** A data set has seven numbers with a range of 12 and a minimum of 20. What is the maximum? Create a possible data set.

   b) Create a different data set with a range of 12 and a minimum of 20 using five different values than you used in Part a.

   c) Create a data set with a range of 12 and a maximum of 3. What must the minimum be?

3. Create a line plot for each of the following data sets. Describe the distribution of each set of data. Include the minimum and maximum values, the range, any gaps, any clusters and a measure of center.

   a) $\{-10, 2, 6, 20, 4, 8\}$

   b) $\{-8.5, -5.5, -3.5, -2.0, -0.25\}$

   c) $\{-\frac{1}{4}, \frac{3}{2}, \frac{5}{4}, 1.5, \frac{7}{16}, \frac{3}{8}, -\frac{2}{8}, \frac{15}{12}, \frac{6}{4}, 0.325, -0.25, \frac{9}{6}\}$

   d) {The set of the first 10 prime numbers}

   e) {The set of all the factors of 81}

   f) $\{3, 3, 3, 3, 3\}$

   g) $\{1, 12, 6, 4, 1, 12, 1, 12, 12, 15, 6, 6, 12, 1\}$

4. The bar graph below shows the data for one eighth grade class collected at the Newtown Sports Academy Magnet School.

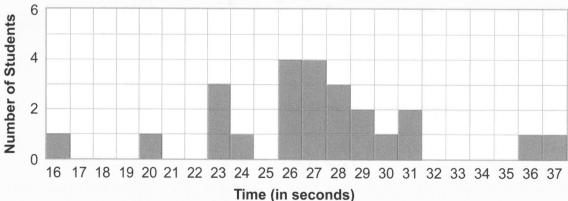

Balancing on One Foot with Eyes Closed

a) Using the graph, describe the distribution of the data.

b) Find a typical value of the data set using a measure of center. Explain why you chose the particular measure.

c) Create a line plot of the same data.

d) Which graph (bar graph or line plot) do you prefer using to analyze the data? Explain.

5. How is a line plot like a bar graph? How is it different?

6. Anthony and Janice are both eighth-graders at Floodbrook Middle School. They each asked nine friends to do the balancing experiment. Below are the data they collected.

Anthony's Friends' Data for Balancing on One Foot

Initials	AV	MG	LC	BS	SG	DS	CK	EZ	TC
Time (sec.)	29	15	24	23	26	24	28	21	29

Janice's Friends' Data for Balancing on One Foot

Initials	JV	KG	SC	LS	SS	EC	MC	BM	EO
Time (sec.)	27	22	36	24	28	27	27	21	26

a) Make a graph (either line plot or bar graph) for each set of data.

b) Find the minimum and maximum values and the range for each set of data.

c) For each set, describe any clusters of data.

d) For each set, describe any gaps in the data.

e) What would be a "typical" length of time for each group? Explain why you chose the particular measure of center.

f) Using the information you found in Parts a–e, compare the two data sets.

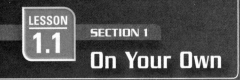
7. Below are two line plots. One line plot shows the times for five of
    Anthony and Janice's friends. The other plot shows the times for one
    student who performed the experiment five times. Which line plot do
    you think belongs to each situation? Explain your reasoning.

    A.

    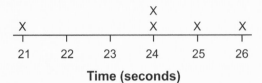

    Time (seconds)

    B.

    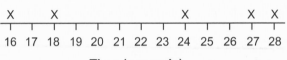

    Time (seconds)

8. Find a chart or graph in a newspaper, a magazine or online. Cut out or
    print the representation. Write down one research question that could
    be answered from the representation and one question related to the
    data that could not be answered from the representation. Describe the
    distribution of the data and answer your first question.

Think Back

9. Last summer, Michelle read a total of 14 sports and science fiction books. The number of sports books was 2 less than 3 times the number of science fiction books that she read. How many of each did she read? Show your work.

10. What is the value of the expression below?

$$(5 \cdot 4)^2 - 5 \cdot 4^2$$

   A. 0   **C.** 320

   B. 180   **D.** 6,320

11. A juice can has a diameter of 2 inches and a height of 6 inches.

   a) How many cans will stand on a base that is 12" × 24"?

   b) If the cans are stacked three deep in a box with a base measuring 12" × 24", how many cans will fit in the box?

   c) What is the total volume of the juice that can fit in this box?

12. Use order of operations to find the value of the following:

$$2 + 2(2 - 2^2) - (2 \cdot 2 + \tfrac{2}{2}) \cdot 2 + 2^3$$

13. **What went wrong?** Peter incorrectly gave the prime factorization of 648 as $2^3 \cdot 9^2$. What was his mistake?

LESSON 1.2 Searching for a Signal—Finding the Mean

 Start It Off

For a week Carrie and Sofia kept track of the number of students on their bus in the morning. They made the following table:

Students Who Ride the Bus

DAY	Number of Students
Monday	21
Tuesday	26
Wednesday	26
Thursday	22
Friday	25

1. What is the mean number of students on the bus that week?

2. What is the median?

3. What is the mode?

You probably learned how to find the mean of a set of numbers when you learned about long division. But did you ever think about *why* you were finding the mean?

Statisticians talk about "noise" when they discuss data. This includes how the data are distributed, the spread of the data, and whether the data have gaps or clusters and other things that come into play when examining data beyond the numbers. They are always looking for a "signal" in the noise to help make sense of the data. Such a "signal" is a measure of center or measure of central tendency.

Statisticians choose to use different measures of center depending on the type of data they are collecting and its distribution. Let's examine when the mean is the most useful measure of center.

Equal Shares

Isabella, Emily, Marcos, Keisha and Troy are collecting bottles to recycle. They plan to divide the bottles equally so they will each receive the same refund when they return them. Below is the number of bottles each collected.

Name	Isabella	Emily	Marcos	Keisha	Troy
Number of bottles	55	64	36	60	45

1. **a)** Without using computation, rearrange the bottles so each student has the same number, by giving some from those students who have more to those students who have less. Explain how you did this.

   b) How many bottles will each person get?

   c) How is this "equal shares" process related to using the computation rule for finding the mean?

2. Judith, another friend, joins the group. She had 40 bottles.

   a) Suppose the six friends share the bottles equally. Redistribute the bottles and determine how many each person will get. Explain what you did.

   b) Compute the mean using the rule.

   c) How do these answers compare?

3. Find the mean of each of the following data sets by redistributing to create equal shares.

   a) {2.5, 1.5, 4, 4}

   b) {23, 30, 13, 42}

   c) {51, 51, 51, 51}

4. With your partner, make up a situation in which it makes sense to find the mean to create equal shares.

5. Hapgood Middle School has students in grades 6, 7 and 8. During the holiday season, the students decided to collect toys to donate to Connecticut Children's Medical Center. The sixth grade class collected 123 toys, and the seventh grade collected 237. The eighth grade also collected toys. If you distributed the toys equally among grades 6 through 8, each class would have contributed 172 toys.

   a) How many toys did the eighth grade collect? Explain how you got your answer.

   b) What is the range for this data set? What is the mean?

6. The fifth grade class at Hapgood Elementary School also collected toys. Their total was 148. You are writing an e-mail to the president of Connecticut Children's Medical Center. In it you want to mention the average number of toys each grade collected. Tamara says you need to take the mean for the middle school grades, 172, add 148 and then divide by 2. Jonas says the resulting number would be too low.

   a) Who is right? Why?

   b) What number will you put in your e-mail? Explain how you found it.

7. Four seventh grade classes at Eastford Middle School each collected toys for the Toys for Tots drive. Their mean number of toys per class was 136.

   a) How many toys might each class have collected?

   b) Could each class have collected the exact same number? If so, what number would that be?

   c) Could exactly one class have collected the same number of toys as the mean? How many toys might the other three classes have collected?

d) Is it possible for three of the classes to have collected a number above the mean? If so, give an example and discuss how the distribution of the data would be affected.

e) Is it possible for all four classes to have collected a number of toys that is less than the mean? If so, give an example and discuss how the distribution of the data would be affected.

8. Can the mean ever be the greatest number in a set of data? The smallest number? Explain.

The Perfect Balance

The mean is also used to indicate a balance point in a set of data. Values on either side of the mean can be compared so that sets of two or more numbers are an equal distance from the mean.

Let's begin by finding the mean of this data set: 4, 0, 8, 13, −3, 12, −4, 2.

We will use the number line below as a balance scale. Use an X to represent each member of the data set. The first X at 0 is already marked for you. The number 4 is the mean and the "balance point."

9. **a)** How many units away from 4 is 0? Can you find a number in the data set that is greater than the mean that is the same distance away from 4?

b) What number in the data set is the same distance away from 4 that 12 is?

c) Look at the remaining three values in the set other than the mean. How do they balance around the mean?

d) Find the sum of the distances from the mean of the numbers below the mean. Compare this with the sum of the distances from the mean of the numbers above the mean.

10. In the data sets below, explain how the values balance around the mean.

a)

b) 5, 10, 15, 17, 18, **20 (mean)**, 25, 30, 40

? Hint
See page 121

11. Hillside Park Market stocks seven different brands of ice cream. The average cost of a half-gallon is $3.49.

a) What might the prices of each of the seven brands be? Use a number line as a balance to help you.

b) Describe the data set you created, including the distribution of the data set, using statistical terms. Find the sum of the differences from the mean for the data above and below the mean.

12. The daily high temperatures for the second week of July in Chicago were 85°, 89°, 84°, 80°, 83°, 85° and 87°.

a) Find the mean daily high temperature for the week.

b) If we added two degrees to each temperature, predict how the mean would change. Explain your reasoning. Find the mean and compare to your prediction.

? Hint
See page 121

c) If we divided each temperature by 2, predict what the mean would be. Find the mean and compare to your prediction. What month might these new temperatures represent?

Wrap It Up

Jenna and Ryan were bowling. In candlepin bowling, each game is called a string. Jenna bowled strings with scores of 116, 159, 136 and 127. Ryan bowled strings with scores of 150, 115, 138, 149 and 125. Talk to your partner and decide who bowled better, even though Ryan bowled one more string than Jenna. Be ready to explain your reasoning using one of the methods that you learned in this lesson.

Write About It

1. Use the equal shares method and the mean as a balancing point on a number line to find the mean in the Start It Off problem.

2. Some friends started a babysitting club. They plan to share their earnings equally after paying for their advertising. For the month of January, Sharon earned $35.25, Jasmine earned $42, Seth earned $51 and Alex earned $25.50. Advertising costs for the month were $26.75.

   a) How much will each friend get?

   b) Describe the data distribution. What is the range? What is the mean?

3. Chandra was away when the babysitting club from Question 2 divided up the money. She had earned $34 for the month. If her earnings are included with the others' earnings and shared equally among the five friends, will the amount they each get be less than, greater than or equal to the total that did not include Chandra's earnings? Explain your reasoning without doing any calculations.

4. Find the mean of each data set without using the computation method (adding and dividing). Show your work.

   a) {6, 6, 6, 6}   c) {3, 3, 6, 12, 4, 8}

   b) {120, 128, 128, 120}   d) {−1, 0, 3, 6, 7, 9, 12, 12}

5. Melissa, Lynn, Don and Jon were talking about the number of people they have in their families. They found that the average number of people in their four families was 5. Create two possible data sets that show how many people each might have in his or her family.

6. Is the mean of a data set always one of the values in the set? Explain your reasoning.

7. Melik said that the average number of people that he and his group of four friends had in their families was 5.2. Jesse said this was impossible since you can't have a fraction of a person! Is Jesse correct? Explain.

8. Explain using the balance point model that the mean of a data set with all the same values is always equal to those values.

9. Below are the scores for one dive for each diver in the Beijing 2008 Diving World Cup Championship. In a competition the divers perform five different dives.

Diving Scores at the Beijing 2008 Diving World Cup Championship

	Judge 1	Judge 2	Judge 3	Judge 4	Judge 5	Judge 6	Judge 7
Christina Loukas (United States)	7.0	7.0	7.0	7.5	6.5	6.5	6.5
Sharleen Stratton (Austria)	8.5	8.5	8.0	8.0	8.0	8.5	8.5
Jing Jing Guo (China)	8.5	8.0	9.0	8.5	9.0	8.5	8.5
Min Xia Wu (China)	9.0	9.0	8.0	9.0	8.5	8.0	9.0
Laura Sanchez (Mexico)	7.5	7.0	8.5	8.0	8.0	8.0	7.5

(Actual scoring for diving at the World Cup Championship is a bit complicated, so we are going to use the mean.)

a) Compare the divers using the mean of the judges' scores.

b) Based on these scores, who do you think came in first, second and third for the competition? Explain your answer.

c) What other information do you need to know to determine who actually placed first, second and third in the competition?

10. Tamika, the star player on the Fermi High School basketball team, has a mean of 15 points per game for the last six games. She scored at least 17 points in each of the first five games. What does this tell you about the number of points she scored in the sixth game?

11. Lee was shopping at Big Saver and found that they carried seven different brands of pretzels in 16 oz. bags. The mean price was $2.12. What might the actual prices of the seven brands be? Show your work.

12. A set of data is made up of five whole numbers. None of these numbers appears more than once. The first three numbers are 2, 3 and 4, and the mean is 3.

a) What could the other two numbers be?

b) If only the numbers 2, 3 or 4 could be used (and could be repeated), what could the other two numbers be?

13. Hallie received the following grades on six math quizzes: 82, 77, 93, 86, 80, 92. She calculated her average to be 85. Today she took a quiz and received an 87. She figured her new average was 86 since the mean of 85 and 87 is 86. Her teacher calculated her average to be 85 (rounded to the nearest whole number).

   a) How did her teacher find this average?

   b) Who is correct? Explain.

14. **What went wrong?** Jocelyn was buying desserts for a party with nine of her friends. Five chocolate frosted brownies cost $1 each, three crème puffs cost $2 each and two lemon tarts cost $3 each. She told her friends the average cost of a dessert was $2. This is how she found the mean: $\left(\frac{1 + 2 + 3}{3}\right)$. She asked each friend to pay $2 and that would make everyone even. What's wrong with her reasoning?

15. Your local newspaper is reporting the results of the National Assessment of Educational Progress (NAEP) mathematics testing. This is a national test given every four years to students in grades 4, 8 and 12. The headlines read, "About half of the eighth-graders in our nation scored below average on the math portion of the NAEP." Explain why these test results are not surprising.

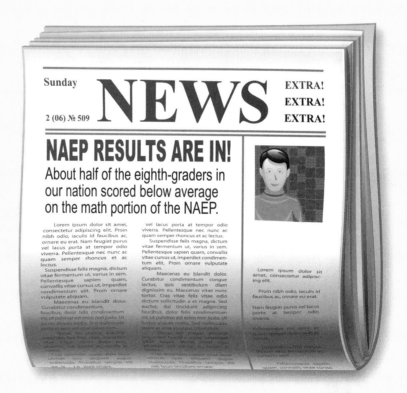

16. Conrad had a mean of 150 after bowling a string of three games.

    a) If he bowls 160 in his fourth game, what is his new average?

    b) If he bowls 160 again in his fifth game, why does this raise his average less than the first 160?

    c) Conrad has an average of B after bowling G games. What is his new average after he bowls 160 in the next game?

17. There is a statistic called the standard deviation that tells us whether or not the data in a set are clustered closely together or spread apart.

    a) Research more information about the standard deviation and what connection it has to the mean and deviation from the mean.

    b) What temperatures would be within one standard deviation of the mean for the temperatures listed in Question 12 in the lesson?

18. Aria works for her dad selling plants. He gives her $5 per hour plus commissions of $2.50 for each bush ($b$) and $1.50 for each hanging plant (h) she sells. Write an expression for the amount she earned in an 8-hour day.

19. South America has an area of 17,780,000 square kilometers. Expressed in scientific notation, this is:

    A. $1,778 \times 10^4$ km^2 **C.** 17.78×10^6 km^2

    B. 177.8×10^5 km^2 **D.** 1.778×10^7 km^2

20. The area of South America expressed in square miles is 6,890,000 sq. mi., or almost 3.5% of the earth's surface. What is the total surface of the earth?

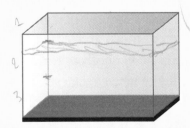

21. Jean's father wanted her to fill a tank $\frac{2}{3}$ full. The tank measures 20 cm $\times$ 30 cm $\times$ 45 cm. How much water does she need? Express your answer in liters (1,000 cm^3 = 1 liter)

22. The following formula is used to find the horsepower of an engine: $p = \frac{nd^2}{2.5}$, where p = power, n = number of cylinders and d = diameter of each cylinder. Find the horsepower of a 6-cylinder engine if each cylinder is $3\frac{1}{2}$ inches in diameter.

Searching for a Signal—Finding the Median

Start It Off

The word *median* is used in different ways in our everyday life. Describe a situation that uses this term. Explain how this might relate to the way we use the term *median* in mathematics.

Another Measure of Center, the Median

Ava's math test scores for the marking period are:

89, 91, 90, 91, 93, 60, 91, 90, 88

Her teacher told her she found the average, 87, and gave Ava a B on her report card.

Ava said this was unfair since eight of her nine scores were higher than 87! She said this does not represent her test scores for the marking period.

1. Talk to your partner. Do you agree with Ava? Explain your answer. If you agree with her, come up with another method for calculating Ava's grade.

Examine the line plot of Ava's test scores below. Notice that most of her scores are clustered together with one exception, 60.

Ava's Test Scores

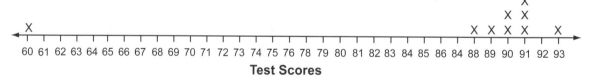

Test Scores

When a data set includes a value that is much less than or much greater than the other data points, the median may describe the data set better than the mean. Remember, the median is the number in the middle when a data set is arranged in order from least to greatest. It divides the data set into two equal halves with as many data points above it as below it.

2. **a)** Find the median of Ava's scores.

    b) Is the median a better measure than the mean of Ava's typical test score? Why or why not?

3. Carlton is trying to find the median for the data plotted below, which are his grades for the marking period. He can't find a middle value in the set! Why not? Talk to your partner and suggest how he might find the median or middle value of his test scores.

Carlton's Test Scores

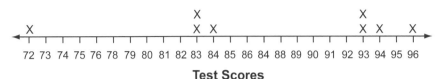

72 73 74 75 76 78 79 80 81 82 83 84 85 86 84 88 89 90 91 92 93 94 95 96

Test Scores

4. Compare Carlton's scores to Ava's scores. Discuss the distribution of the data, any clusters or gaps and the "typical" score for each.

The Take-Away Store sells a variety of Fruit Smoothies in different flavors. Gordon and Kalena wanted to see if there were differences in the numbers of calories for the various drinks. They created the list below to show the number of calories in an 8-ounce serving of several different drinks.

Take-Away Fruit Smoothies

Type of Smoothie	Number of Calories
Melon Blast	65
Strawberry Ice	63
Cranberry Cooler	60
Coconut Crush	70
Gonzilla Grape	118
Arctic Cherry	40
Plum Pudding	65
Colossal Kiwi	55
Banana Split	70

5. a) Make a line plot of the fruit drinks data.

   b) Describe the distribution of the data (that is, minimum value, maximum value, range, gaps, clusters).

   c) Do you think the mean and median will be close together or far apart? Explain your answer.

   d) Find the mean and median and indicate where each is on the line plot. Were you correct?

   e) The Diet Melon Blast has 0 calories. If you add this flavor to the table above, predict how this will affect the distribution of the data. How will it affect the mean? The median? Will they still be close together? Which will be higher?

   f) Now find the mean and median and see if you were correct.

6. Without computing the mean, state whether the mean or the median would be the higher value in each of these data sets. How can you tell?

a) 32, 21, 8, 28, 30, 25, 30, 25

b) 190, 175, 160, 160, 165, 163, 192, 165, 183

c) 23.9, 23.5. 23.8, 24.1, 24, 24.2

Creating Stem-and-Leaf Plots

We can present numerical data in a display called a stem-and-leaf plot. The data values must be numerical. The stem represents a particular place value, such as tens or hundreds of each number. The leaves are the remaining place values arranged from least to greatest. This is indicated in a key as part of the display. Below is a stem-and-leaf plot of the data set in Question 6a.

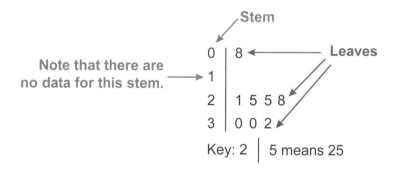

Note that 0 8 represents the number 8 (0 tens and 8 ones). It is easy to see that the minimum value is 8 and the maximum value is 32. Also, since the data are arranged in order, you can easily find the median, which is halfway between 25 and 28. You can see that 8 is separated from most of the data, which affects the mean. The majority of the data are clustered in the 25 to 30 range.

7. Make a stem-and-leaf plot for Parts b and c of Question 6. First, decide which place value will be your stem. Make sure to include a key. Describe the data set using your stem-and-leaf plot.

8. Make a stem-and-leaf plot for all the Take-Away Fruit Smoothies data (including the Diet Melon Blast). Note that one piece of data is a three-digit number rather than a two-digit number.

a) What place value did you use for your stem? Make sure to include a key.

b) Which display do you prefer, the line plot or the stem-and-leaf plot? Explain.

Wrap It Up

Discuss when the median might be a better way to describe a "typical" value in a data set than the mean. Create a data set for which you would use the median to describe the "typical" value and another data set where it would not make a difference whether you used the mean or the median.

Write About It

1. Suppose you have five piles of CDs with 5, 4, 7, 9 and 5 CDs in each pile.

   a) If you wanted to order the piles to show the median number of CDs in a pile, how would you do it?

   b) If you rearrange the CDs so that each pile has the same number of CDs in it, how many will be in each pile? What type of measure of center are you using? Explain how you know.

2. Construct data sets composed of different values for each of the following characteristics.

   a) The mean and median are the same value.

   b) The mean is higher than the median.

   c) The median is higher than the mean.

3. Five friends each earn $100 per week mowing lawns.

   a) Without using computation, find the *average* amount each friend earned per week.

   b) How will using the mean as a measure of center in this situation compare with using the median?

   c) Daryl's older brother also mowed lawns and earned $350 per week. If you include Daryl's brother in the data set to find the average earnings per mower, which statistic is affected: the mean or the median? Explain.

4. Without doing any computation, which would be the higher value: the mean age or the median age of everyone in your math class, including your teacher? Explain your answer.

5. Cheryl thinks the median has to be a number in the data set since it represents the middle of the set. Do you agree? Why or why not?

6. Create a stem-and-leaf plot for the following two data sets that each describe incomes in thousands (for example, 68 represents $68,000) for a group of people that live in the same state and then describe the distribution of the data in each set.

   a) 68, 31, 44, 40, 42, 30, 52, 85, 56, 23, 39, 48, 42, 30

   b) 141, 64, 35, 56, 59, 42, 38, 40, 35, 67, 54, 110, 64, 36, 62, 55, 71

7. Compare the two data sets that describe income in Question 6, discussing the distribution of the data and measures of center.

8. Listed below are some state income levels for 2006. If all the values in each data set in Question 6 above were representative of people living in the same state in 2006, which state would each group most likely be living in? Explain your answer.

2006 State Income Levels

State	Median Income Level
Alabama	$38,160
Connecticut	$60,551
Kansas	$44,478
New Jersey	$66,752
Nevada	$51,036
Pennsylvania	$48,148
South Carolina	$40,583

9. You are a statistician who will report on the salaries for eight town employees in Compton. The salaries are: $40,000; $45,000; $44,000; $50,000; $72,000; $42,000; $71,000; $64,000.

   a) The town finance board wants to show that these salaries are adequate and no increase in pay is needed. To support this view, which measure of center would you use: the mean or median? Explain your answer.

   b) The employees' union wants to show that the average salary is low and an increase is needed. To support this view, which measure of center would you use: the mean or median? Explain your answer.

10. **a)** Which would be higher, the mean height or the median height of the people in the photograph?

b) Which person(s) would you remove from the photo so that the mean and median would be close to the same?

Photo courtesy of M. Katherine Gavin.

11. Jeff's Cookie Corner at the Discovery Center has six employees. Jeff says the typical salary is $45,000. The workers say the typical salary is $35,000. Make up a set of data that show that both Jeff and his workers are correct.

 **Think Beyond**

12. Can two sets of data have the same mean and median values, and yet be very different? If so, give an example. If not, explain why not.

13. Marilyn and her cousin Danny are hoping to go shopping to buy their favorite computer games. Marilyn has already saved $\frac{2}{3}$ of the $63 she needs for her game and Danny has saved $\frac{5}{8}$ of the $56 he needs.

    a) How much has each one saved?

    b) Who will get their game first if they can each save another $5 per week? How many weeks will it take? Write an equation for each using x for the number of weeks.

14. This graph could represent which set of values listed below?

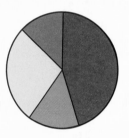

   A. Blue = 55; Red = 45; Yellow = 35; Green = 10

   B. Blue = 90; Red = 30; Yellow = 54; Green = 26

   C. Blue = 55; Red = 5; Yellow = 35; Green = 10

   D. Blue = 55; Red = 25; Yellow = 35; Green = 40

15. **What went wrong?**
    Lew had to find the answer to $126 = 0.5\%$ of _____.
    He multiplied $0.005 \cdot 126$ and got 0.63. He knew that 0.63 was too small. What went wrong?

16. Which of the following is equivalent to the expression below?
    $$2(7x - 11) - (x - 8)$$

   A. $13x - 14$ **C.** $15x - 30$

   B. $13x - 30$ **D.** $-15x - 14$

17. The modern era of the summer Olympics began in 1896. There were no games in 1916, 1940 or 1944 due to World Wars I and II.

    a) As of 2008, how many summer Olympics had there been in the modern era?

    b) The games were held in the United States in 1904 in St. Louis, in 1932 and 1984 in Los Angeles, and in 1996 in Atlanta. Of the summer Olympics that occurred in the modern era, what percent were held in the United States?

Optional Technology Lesson for this section available in your eBook

Sum It Up

In this section, you learned how statisticians use mathematics to help tell the story about a set of data. You revisited the mean, median and mode as measures of center. You learned how to describe the distribution of the data using the maximum and minimum values, the range and clusters and gaps in the data. You learned how to create a stem-and-leaf plot to help organize data. You created and analyzed bar graphs, line plots and tables to display the data for easy interpretation.

The important ideas in this section include:

- When describing the **distribution of a data set**, the following are used:

  - **Minimum** (the least value in the data set) and **maximum** (the greatest value in the data set) values

  - **Range** (the difference between the maximum and minimum values)

  - **Gaps** (an interval in which there are no data values)

  - **Clusters** (data values which are grouped closely together)

- **Measures of center**, also known as **measures of central tendency**, describe the typical value in a data set. These include the **mean, median** and **mode**. Each of these is a numerical value that describes the overall "average" of the data set in a particular way.

  - Two different ways to think about the **mean** are as distributing equal shares or creating a balance point.

    - The **equal shares** method focuses on redistributing values in the set until all values become the same value (the mean).

    - The **balance point** method focuses on the mean as a balance point on a balance scale. The sum of the distances from data points above the mean to the mean is the same as the sum of the distances from data points below the mean to the mean. This means that the scale balances.

    - The rule for calculating the mean is to add all the values in the data set and then divide by the number of values in the set.

- The **median** is the value that divides the data set into two equal halves with as many data points above it as below it. It may or may not be a member of the data set.
  - If there is an odd number of values in the data set, the median is the middle value when the data are put in order from least to greatest.
  - If there is an even number of values in the data set, the median is the arithmetic average of the two middle values.
- The **mode** is the most frequent value in the data set. If there are two values that occur most frequently, the set is said to be **bimodal**.

■ Two different ways to graph data are:

- A **line plot** can be used to show the number of occurrences of data values. This is generally used with a small data set since each member of the set is recorded with an X above a number line. Using the line plot, you can find the median and mode and describe the distribution of the data indicating the range, gaps and clusters. You can also calculate the mean using the information displayed. Below is an example of a line plot.

Number of Seconds Balancing on One Foot

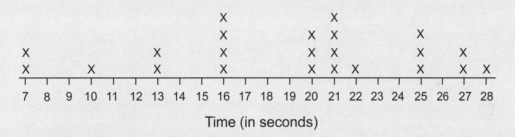

Time (in seconds)

- **Stem-and-leaf plots** can be used to organize numerical data from least to greatest. The stem represents a particular place value, such as tens or hundreds of each number. The leaves are the remaining place values arranged in order from least to greatest. This arrangement is indicated in a key. Below is an example of a stem-and-leaf plot.

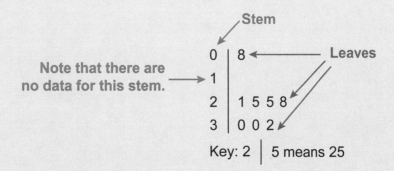

MATHEMATICALLY SPEAKING

Do you know what these mathematical terms mean?

- bimodal
- clusters
- data
- data analysis
- descriptive statistics
- distribution of data
- gaps
- line plot
- mean
- measures of center (or of central tendency)
- median
- mode
- range
- statistics
- stem-and-leaf plot

Part 1. What did you learn?

1. Find the data set in Column B that matches the correct description in Column A.

Description	Data Set
a. This data set is bimodal.	**i.** 1, 2, 3, 4, 6, 17, 18, 19
b. The median of this data set is not a whole number.	**ii.** 1, 2, 3, 3, 3, 5, 6, 9
c. The median of this data set is the same as the mode.	**iii.** 1, 1, 2, 3, 3, 5, 7, 9
d. There is a large gap in this data set.	**iv.** 2, 3, 3, 4, 5, 7, 8, 9

2. Larissa asked 20 students in her class to keep track of the number of minutes they spend eating breakfast each morning. Her data set is {1, 1, 1, 2, 2, 2, 2, 2, 2, 2, 2, 3, 3, 3, 3, 5, 5, 5, 6, 20}.

    a. Find the range of Larissa's data set.

    b. Find the median.

    c. Find the mean.

    d. Do you think the median or the mean is a better representation of the data set? Explain.

3. For each of the following data sets, predict (without calculation) whether the median will be less than ($<$) or greater than ($>$) the mean.

    a. 40, 42, 45, 49, 50, 51, 194

    b. 0.089, 3.2, 3.5, 4.0, 4.2, 4.5

    c. 0, 150, 160, 160, 175, 176

4. Create a data set of exactly four whole-number values with a mean of 3.5.

5. Create a data set of exactly four non-whole-number values with a median of 4.

6. Find the mean of the data set {−2, 3, 0, 10, 8, −1} using the equal shares method. Show your work.

7. Find the mean of the data set {4, 6, 7, 10, 12, 20, 25} using the balancing point method. Show your work.

8. Dana wants to find out how many letters people receive each week. She asked 25 neighbors to keep track of the number of letters they received one week. Her data set is {5, 5, 7, 9, 11, 11, 14, 14, 14, 15, 16, 17, 19, 19, 22, 24, 27, 27, 30, 32, 40, 45, 48, 52, 53}.

   a. Create a stem-and-leaf plot of Dana's data set.

   b. Describe the distribution of the data. Identify any gaps or clusters.

   c. What is the "typical" number of letters that Dana's neighbors receive?

   d. Did you use the mean, median, mode or another value to answer Part c? Why?

9. Alfonso asked his neighbors how many times they go to the supermarket each week. His data set is {1, 1, 1, 1, 2, 2, 2, 2, 2, 2, 3, 3, 4, 5, 5, 7, 7}.

   a. Create a line plot of his data set.

   b. Describe the distribution of the data. Identify any gaps or clusters.

   c. What is the "typical" number of trips to the supermarket taken by Alfonso's neighbors each week.

10. You made a stem-and-leaf plot for Dana's data set in Question 8 and a line plot of Alfonso's data set in Question 9. Would it make sense to make a line plot of Dana's data set and a stem-and-leaf plot for Alfonso's data set? Why or why not?

11. Denise was asked to calculate the median of the following data set: {3, 7, 2, 8, 4, 10, 5}. Denise wrote, "The median is 8 because that is the number in the middle of the data set." Denise's answer was marked wrong. Why? What doesn't Denise understand about finding the median?

12. Johan was asked to find the range of the data set below.

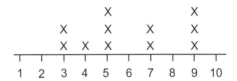

He wrote, "The range is 9. The lowest value shown is 1 and the highest is 10. Then 10 − 1 = 9." What doesn't Johan understand about the range? What is the range of the given data set?

SECTION 2

Organizing, Displaying and Comparing Data

When conducting a research study, it is important to consider how to best represent the data. Your representation will influence how people interpret the information you present. Different types of data sets lend themselves to different representations.

In this section you will use different displays to organize and present data. You will also see how some displays can help people compare two or more data sets and make good decisions based on these comparisons.

LESSON 2.1 Choosing an Appropriate Graph

 **Start It Off**

1. **a)** Using the following graph, which are the two most popular toppings?

   b) The two least popular? How do you know?

   c) How many people do not have a favorite yogurt topping?

Favorite Yogurt Toppings

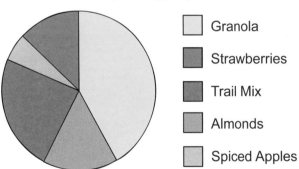

- Granola
- Strawberries
- Trail Mix
- Almonds
- Spiced Apples

2. Estimate the percent of people who chose each option. Discuss your choices with your partner and see if you agree. Be sure the percents add to 100%!

3. If the circle graph above represents the favorite toppings of 60 students, approximately how many students selected each category?

Ms. Solomon sponsors a child in Ethiopia. In an e-mail from the Child Relief Organization, they told her how her first $100 donation was spent. They included a circle graph with the same information.

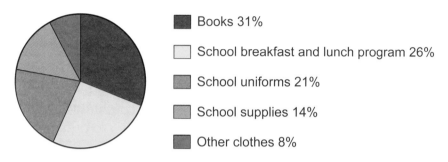

- ■ Books 31%
- □ School breakfast and lunch program 26%
- ■ School uniforms 21%
- ■ School supplies 14%
- ■ Other clothes 8%

Ms. Solomon decided to discuss this graph with her eighth grade class. How would you respond to the following questions she asked her class?

1. What is the dollar amount spent for each category? Why is this easy to determine?

2. Could you display this information in a line plot? Why or why not?

3. a) Could you display this information in a bar graph? Why or why not?

The type of information displayed in this graph is categorical. Data that have specific labels and can be categorized or put into groups are called categorical data.

By contrast, the type of data we used in the last section was mainly numerical data. Numerical data have number values (for example, age, test score, temperature, distance, time).

   b) Finding a mean or median does not make sense when you are dealing with categorical data. Why?

A circle graph is a good representation for these data since the categories are all parts of one whole. When looking at the circle graph, you can easily tell which category has the greatest percentage. Using the percents assigned to the sections of the circle, you can determine how much is being spent on each of the categories. In this case, converting from percents to dollars is easy.

4. Now it's your turn! If you had $150 to spend on whatever you chose, how would you spend it?

- As a class, decide on four or five categories in which to spend the money.

- Next, individually decide on the dollar amounts you would spend in each of those categories. Create a circle graph. Make sure you create a title for the graph and labels for each of the categories. (You can use a computer program such as Excel to help you.)

5. Next, analyze the data. In groups of four, use your graphs to compare how each student in your group would spend the money.

a) Approximately what percent of the $150 would each of you spend in each of the categories?

b) Approximately how much money would each of you spend in each of the categories?

c) Would any of you spend the same amount of money in a category?

d) Write a paragraph describing how the students in your group would spend the money, using information from the four circle graphs.

6. Martin's group decided to create the bar graph below to display their data.

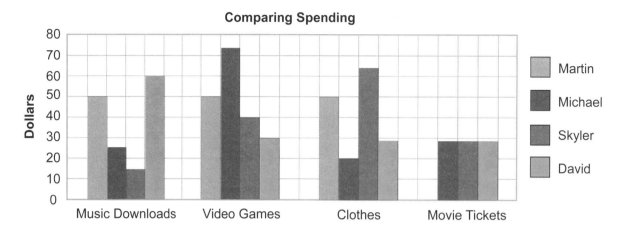

Comparing Spending

a) How much money would Martin spend on video games?

b) How much money would Skyler spend on clothes?

c) Who would spend the most money on music downloads?

d) Would each student spend some money in every category? If not, describe the situation.

e) What percent of Martin's money would be spent on music downloads?

7. Compare using a bar graph to using a circle graph when analyzing data. What are the advantages and disadvantages of each type of display?

Different Data Displays—Different Stories to Tell

You know how to make different types of displays including line plots, bar graphs, tables, stem-and-leaf plots and circle graphs. As a researcher, it is important to determine which type of display best represents the data. You should select a graph or table that:

- best shows the results, including comparisons among data values,

- can be interpreted easily by your audience, and

- is free from bias or misinterpretations.

Let's look at three data displays and see the story that is told by each. These displays each give population data for the New England States from the 2000 Census. You will need to complete the table.

Circle Graph

2000 Census Population of New England States

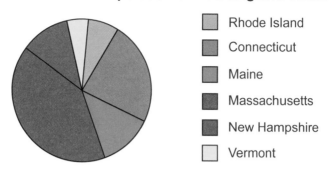

- Rhode Island
- Connecticut
- Maine
- Massachusetts
- New Hampshire
- Vermont

Table

| 2000 Census Population of New England States ||
State	Population
	3,405,565
Maine	1,274,923
	6,349,097
	1,235,786
Rhode Island	1,048,319
	608,827

Histogram

Population of the New England States U.S. Census 2000

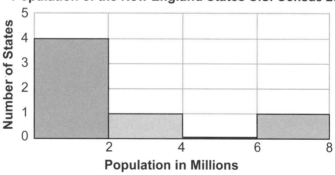

Let's Review

This last graph is called a histogram. This type of graph is used with data that are grouped into numerical intervals.

- The height of each bar indicates the frequency of the values in that specified interval;
- The intervals all have equal widths; and
- The bars touch each other.

In the case of the histogram above, one interval has no values, and that is represented by the darkened line segment on the *x*-axis.

Use the above three data displays of New England population to respond to the following questions.

8. **a)** Which displays use categorical data? Which displays use numerical data?

   b) Fill in the table with names of states that correspond to the population given. Which display did you use to help you? Why?

   c) Order the New England states from least population to greatest population.

   d) Which data display did you use to determine the order?

9. **a)** Estimate the percent that each state's population represents of New England's total population. Which data display did you use?

   b) Add a column to the table to display the percent of the total New England population that each state's population represents. How do these values compare with your estimates?

10. Which data display(s) shows:

    a) The location of clusters?

    b) The location of gaps?

    c) The median population?

11. Work with a partner to analyze the different representations. Answer the following:

    a) Discuss the limitations of each display.

    b) What is the difference between a bar graph and a histogram?

    c) What advantages does the table have over the circle graph? Over the histogram?

    d) What advantage does the circle graph have over the table?

Choosing the Best Display to Represent the Data

THINKING LIKE A MATHEMATICIAN

When choosing a display that bests represents a situation or a set of data, consider the following:

- Are you showing percents, or parts of a whole?
- Are you showing the frequency of certain categories or numbers?
- Will you list each item and its corresponding numerical entry?
- How large is the data set? Which type of display works best for this size of data set?

12. Talk to your partner and decide on an appropriate graphical representation for each situation below.

   a) Choose from a bar graph, a histogram, a circle graph, a stem-and-leaf plot, a line plot or a table. (Note: There may be more than one appropriate way to display the data.)

   b) Write down your reasoning for your choice.

   c) Share and compare choices as a class.

Situation 1 The time (in seconds) it takes for each person in the class to push an orange with his/her nose across a room

Situation 2 In the game of Family Feud, contestants were asked to name a person that Batman knows but would not invite to his wedding if he were getting married. Survey Says: Joker 58; Catwoman 17; Riddler 13; and Penguin, 12

Situation 3 The ages of teachers in your middle school

Situation 4 The number of days each student in your math class has been absent this month

Situation 5 When asked, "What did you do yesterday?" 15–21-year-olds in the United States, Hong Kong and Shanghai responded in the following way:

Read a magazine: United States—20%, Hong Kong—65%, Shanghai—81%

Accessed the Internet: United States—75%, Hong Kong—72%, Shanghai—75%

Watched TV: United States—68%, Hong Kong—19%, Shanghai—15%

Went to a movie: United States—6%, Hong Kong—34%, Shanghai—26%

Interesting data about teenagers all over the world can be found in the online magazine *Trends & Tudes*.

13. Work with a partner. Find some data in this magazine or another online source that can be displayed in a different (and perhaps better) way than is presented. Create a display to share with the class. In writing:

a) Explain why you chose your data and the type of display.

b) Tell the story of the data (analyze the data using your display).

c) Describe something that surprised you when analyzing the data.

 **rap It Up**

In a small group, discuss the advantages and disadvantages of the representations listed below and the types of data best displayed by each representation. Your teacher will assign you a type of graph to report on to the class.

a) circle graph

b) bar graph

c) table

d) stem-and-leaf plot

e) histogram

f) line plot

Write About It

1. A new student has just entered your class. Prepare a written set of notes to help her understand the difference between a line plot, a circle graph, a stem-and-leaf plot and a histogram. You may want to use outline form or a chart to organize the notes.

2. This table shows the days of the month in January and the high temperature recorded for each day.

January Temperatures			
Day	Temp. (°F)	Day	Temp. (°F)
1	24	17	34
2	27	18	38
3	24	19	45
4	34	20	21
5	38	21	24
6	38	22	27
7	27	23	32
8	17	24	32
9	8	25	21
10	17	26	32
11	33	27	27
12	34	28	24
13	33	29	21
14	38	30	27
15	32	31	30
16	33		

Nina thought a line plot would be the best way to display these data. Alan thought a stem-and-leaf plot would be the best way. Explain the advantages of each representation.

3. Choose either a line plot or stem-and-leaf plot and create a display for the temperatures in Question 2.

4. a) If you were a meteorologist, how would you describe the distribution of the temperatures for the month of January from Question 2?

   b) In what part of the United States might these temperatures have been recorded?

5. **a)** If you surveyed your classmates to find out which month they were born in, would you use a line plot or bar graph to display the data? Explain.

b) If you surveyed your classmates to find out which day of the month they were born on, would you use a line plot or bar graph to display the data? Explain.

Think Beyond

c) What information would you like to know about your classmates? Write a research question to gather that information and conduct a survey. Display the data using an appropriate graph and write up your results using the graph.

6. A survey asked middle school students to identify their favorite subject. The results were: Language Arts, 246; Math, 275; Science, 201; and Spanish, 133.

a) What additional information would a circle graph representing these data give you?

b) What information would probably not be included in the circle graph that could be shown in a bar graph?

c) Would a line plot be appropriate? Why or why not?

d) Would a histogram be appropriate? Why or why not?

7. Create a representation of your choice for the data in Question 6 and write a paragraph analyzing the data based on your representation.

8. Choose the most appropriate display for the data below. Choose from line plot, histogram, circle graph or bar graph. Choose each type of graph only once.

a) The percent of electricity produced from different sources in the United States.

b) The number of times per week eighth-graders in your school use e-mail, recorded in intervals of 1–4, 5–8, and so on.

c) The number of almonds in each of 30 small packages of nuts.

d) Your classmates' favorite singers.

9. Which representations provide the information needed for you to find the median? The mode? The mean?

10. Which representations will allow you to easily identify clusters? Gaps? The range?

Think Beyond

11. Learn how to use your graphing calculator to create a histogram. Using your calculator, create a histogram of the population of the states bordering the East Coast of the United States from Maine to Florida as recorded in the 2000 U.S. Census.

Think Back

12. Life in the kingdom of Arcadia was peaceful, at least for the dragon. He just spotted two cylindrical creatures that looked great for an evening snack. The dragon decided to eat the larger one. If creature A has a height of 5' and a radius of 4" and creature B has a height of 6' and a radius of 3", which one should the dragon eat?

13. Life in the kingdom of Arcadia was anything but peaceful for the Queen. A dragon swooped down and kidnapped her husband! The Queen decided to make banners summoning a hero to rescue her husband. There were two banner printers in the kingdom. The Medieval Lettering Company charges 40 copper coins for the first 15 words and 2 copper coins for each additional word. The Words-R-Good Company charges 15 copper coins for the first 10 words and 3 copper coins for each additional word.

   a) If the Queen wants to put 27 words on her banners, which company will charge less?

   b) How many words would the Queen have to use for the companies to charge the same price?

Think Back

14. The Queen's plea for help was answered by the legendary Erica Valiant. Erica promised the Queen that she would rescue the King. The Queen promised to pay Erica her weight in gold. If the density of gold is 19.3 grams per cubic centimeter and Erica weighs 75 kilograms, what is the volume of the gold she will receive?

15. Erica went to the nearest stables for transportation and found two animals for sale: an elderly horse and a young donkey. The owner told her that the horse can trot at 8 miles per hour but needs to rest for one hour after every 3.5 hours of travel. The donkey can go 7 miles per hour but only needs to rest for one half hour after every 5.5 hours of travel. If Erica plans to travel 18 hours a day, which animal will take her farther in one day? How much farther will that animal take her?

Think Beyond

16. After a few days' travel, Erica came to the dragon's cave. The dragon was nowhere to be seen, but Erica saw that the King was locked inside a wooden cage. Erica figured she could use the rocks in the cave to break the cage by smashing them down against the bars. The force of the blow is equal to the weight of the rock multiplied by how high above the bar she can lift it. She can lift a rock six feet up, minus a distance equal to one-third the weight of the rock. There are 4 rocks on the ground, weighing 12 lb., 9 lb., 6 lb. and 3 lb., respectively. Which rock will deliver the most force? How much force will that be?

Box-and-Whisker Plots

Start It Off

Death Valley, California, is one of the hottest places on Earth. The following chart shows the average high temperatures by month for one location in Death Valley.

Month	Average High Temperature (°F)
January	64.6
February	72.3
March	80.4
April	89.8
May	99.3
June	109.0
July	115.3
August	113.2
September	105.8
October	92.0
November	75.7
December	65.1

1. What is the maximum average high temperature for the year?

2. What is the minimum average high temperature for the year?

3. What is the median for the average high temperature for the year?

4. How does this compare to the mean? Were you expecting the mean to be close to the median? Explain.

The Five-Number Summary

We used line plots to represent some of the data sets in the first section. They are a good representation of the distribution of data. On a line plot, we can easily find the median and see extreme values, clusters or gaps.

Another display that highlights the median, shows the distribution of data and is frequently used to compare data sets is a box-and-whisker plot. To create a box-and-whisker plot, or box plot, statisticians first calculate the five-number summary, which includes five measures associated with a data set:

MATHEMATICALLY SPEAKING

- ▶ box-and-whisker plot (box plot)
- ▶ five-number summary

1) The minimum value

2) The first quartile (or lower quartile). This is the median of the scores below the median of the data set. It is labeled Q1.

3) The median value of the data set, which is sometimes labeled Q2

4) The third quartile (or upper quartile). This is the median of the scores above the median of the data set. It is labeled Q3.

5) The maximum value

Mr. Marolda wants to see if his eighth-grade students understand the math concepts from a chapter they have just completed. The following is the set of chapter test scores for his class of 20 eighth-graders.

{96, 72, 94, 85, 56, 76, 90, 81, 74, 85, 83, 84, 81, 75, 76, 72, 73, 70, 68, 94}

To analyze the data, you can use the five-number summary. To find the values in the summary, first order the data values from smallest to largest. While some prefer to use a line plot, we have chosen to use a stem-and-leaf plot to organize the data.

1. The minimum value is _____.

2. The maximum value is _____.

3. The median is 78.5. How did we arrive at this number?

4. The first or lower quartile is the median of all numbers below the median of the whole set (78.5). Find this number.

5. The third or upper quartile is the median of all the numbers above the median of the whole set (78.5). Find this number.

6. List the five-number summary in order: minimum value, Q1, median (Q2), Q3 and maximum value.

To represent these data and the statistics you have just found, you can use a box-and-whisker plot. (You may be wondering about the "whisker," but you'll see why we use that name shortly.)

- Draw a number line starting at 55 and continuing to 100. The division of the number line is up to you and should make sense depending on your data values. Here, we use intervals of 5.

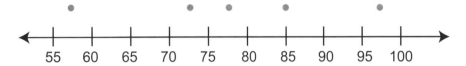

- Mark dots above the number line to represent the points for your minimum, median, maximum and lower and upper quartiles.

- Draw a box between the two quartiles. Mark the median with a vertical segment in the box. Then draw the two "whiskers" from the quartiles to the extreme values (the minimum and the maximum).

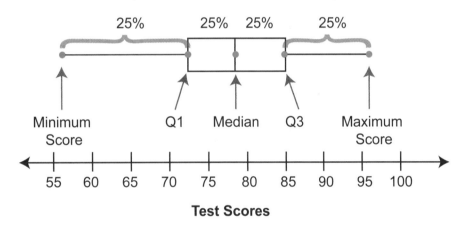

Test Scores

Q1 is 72.5, the median is 78.5 and Q3 is 85.

Notice that the quartiles are the upper or lower boundary values of the quarters. Twenty-five percent, or one quarter, of the data set lie in each of the labeled sections. The box represents the middle 50% of the data.

7. Mr. Marolda needs to analyze the data in order to find out if his students understood the chapter. Help him by answering the following questions.

   a) What is the range of scores?

   b) Why is one whisker longer than the other?

   c) Look at the box, which contains 50% of the scores. Are these scores symmetrical about the median? Explain your answer.

   d) What measures of center cannot be determined using a box plot?

8. Mr. Marolda needs to draw conclusions from the data. If you were Mr. Marolda, would you move on to the next chapter or reteach the concepts that were covered in this chapter to the class? Explain your answer.

Comparing Data Sets

Plotting two box-and-whisker plots on the same number line is a good way to compare and analyze two sets of data. At a glance, you can see how the spreads of the data, medians, minimums and maximums compare.

Examine Ms. Spinelli's set of eighth-grade test scores on the same math test. The data set for these scores is:
{84, 92, 78, 76, 93, 97, 84, 91, 94, 88, 77, 71, 82, 95, 78, 87, 89, 85, 86, 72}.

9. Create a stem-and-leaf plot for this data set. Then find the five-number summary and draw a box-and-whisker plot on the same number line as Mr. Marolda's test scores.

10. Write a paragraph comparing the test results of the two classes. Discuss the medians, the minimum and maximum values and the spread of the data. Which class performed better?

Outliers

MATHEMATICALLY SPEAKING

▶ outliers

▶ interquartile range

In Section 1, we talked about data set values that are far from the mean and median and do not represent the data set as a whole. These are called outliers. To see if a value is an outlier, we first calculate the interquartile range (the difference between the upper quartile and the lower quartile) and then multiply this number by 1.5. Any value whose distance is more than 1.5 times the interquartile range above the upper quartile or below the lower quartile is considered an outlier.

The data below show the annual salaries of employees of Tech Experts, a small technology firm.

Tech Experts Employees' Salaries	
Job	**Annual Salary**
President	$400,000
Executive Assistant	$60,000
Sales Representative	$150,000
Marketing Director	$90,000
Technical Support Technician	$80,000
Administrative Assistant	$45,000
Junior Sales Representative	$92,000
Research and Development Director	$100,000
Computer Programmer	$115,000

11. **a)** Find the five-number summary of this data set.

b) Looking at the data, do you think there are any outliers? Explain your reasoning.

c) To find an outlier, first calculate the interquartile range. To do this, find the difference between Q3 and Q1. Multiply this difference by 1.5. What is this value?

d) Add this value to the value of the upper quartile. Subtract this value from the value of the lower quartile. Are there any outliers?

e) Create a box-and-whisker plot for this data set.

(These instructions are for the TI84+ calculator.)

Now let's create a box-and-whisker plot for the data in Question #11 using a graphing calculator.

Step 1. Choose [STAT 1 EDIT] Enter the data in [L1].

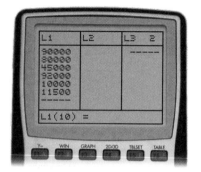

Step 2. Press [2nd] [STAT PLOT] and choose #1 [PLOT 1].
Turn plot to [ON], choose the first box-and-whisker icon.
Make sure [L1] is indicated next to [XLIST].
Freq:1 means that each piece of data will be counted once.

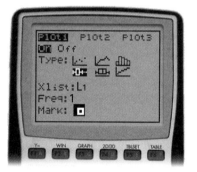

Step 3. To see the box-and-whisker plot, press [ZOOM] and then #9 [ZOOM STAT].

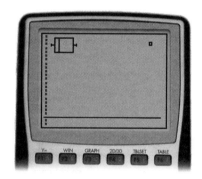

Step 4. Press the [TRACE] key to see information about the plot. The "spider" will jump from the minimum value to Q1 to the median to Q3 and to the maximum value.

12. **a)** How does this box-and-whisker plot differ from the ones that you created by hand?

b) Why do you think the plot is displayed this way?

13. Use your graphing calculator and recreate the box plots for Mr. Marolda's and Ms. Spinelli's test grades on the same graph. From the graph, determine if there are any outliers. Explain your answer.

Your Turn!

Yogurt-covered raisins are packaged by weight. Do you think all boxes of the same weight contain the same number of raisins? Does it depend on the brand?

Let's investigate. As a class, you will analyze several boxes from three different brands and fill in the chart below.

Number of Raisins								
Brand Name	Box 1	Box 2	Box 3	Box 4	Box 5	Box 6	Box 7	Box 8

Your teacher will divide the class into three groups representing the three brands. Groups will receive eight boxes of raisins and count the number of raisins in each box. Each group will then find the five-number summary and make a box-and-whisker plot. Groups will also find any outliers.

14. Create one graph that shows the box-and-whisker plots of the three brands.

    a) Compare the data using the box-and-whisker plots. Discuss the medians, Q1, Q3, outliers, if any, and the size of the boxes.

    b) Which brand would you buy? Do you want many raisins in a box or fewer but larger ones?

    c) For which brand is the number of raisins in a box most consistent? Explain.

 **W**rap It Up

How can the information in a box plot help you tell the story about the data? What information does a box-and-whisker plot give that is different from the information given by a stem-and-leaf plot or a line plot? Discuss these questions with your partner and then share with the class.

MATHEMATICALLY SPEAKING

▸ box-and-whisker plot (box plot)

▸ first or lower quartile, Q1

▸ five-number summary

▸ interquartile range

▸ outliers

▸ third or upper quartile, Q3

 **Write About It**

1. Four different calculator views of the same box-and-whisker plot are shown. The data represent the number of calories in 15 different beverages. The cursor "X" is placed at various positions on the plot to display different information.

   a) What information do the various views of this graph tell you about the data?

   b) What additional information would you like to know?

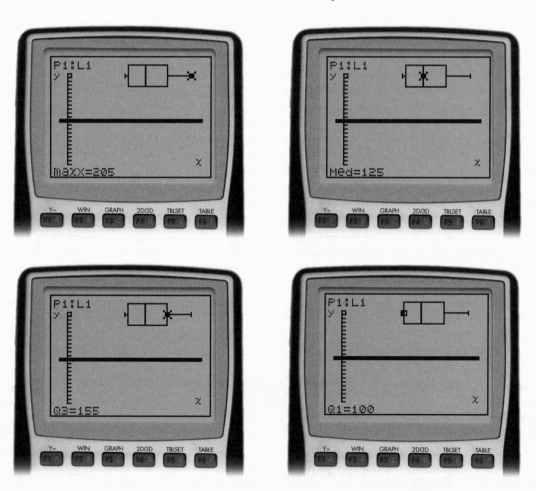

2. Use the data about the average high temperatures in Death Valley, California, from the Start It Off to create a box-and-whisker plot. Tell the story about these data using information in the box-and-whisker plot.

3. Becky kept track of how many points she scored in each of the 25 basketball games her team played this past season. She used a line plot to display the data.

Number of Points Scored in a Basketball Game

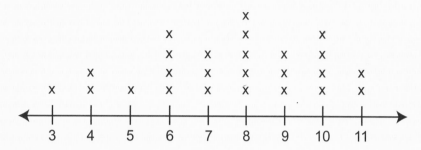

a) Using the line plot, find the five-number summary of the data set.

b) Create a box-and-whisker plot.

c) What does the box-and-whisker plot show that the line plot does not?

d) From the line plot, we can determine that Becky scored 8 points in five of her games. Does a box-and-whisker plot show this information as well?

e) Which data representation do you prefer? Explain your answer.

4. What are the advantages of using a box-and-whisker plot to compare two data sets?

5. The National Basketball Association (NBA) has teams in four divisions. The following box-and-whisker plot shows the average NBA ticket prices for the 2003–2004 season.

NBA Ticket Prices

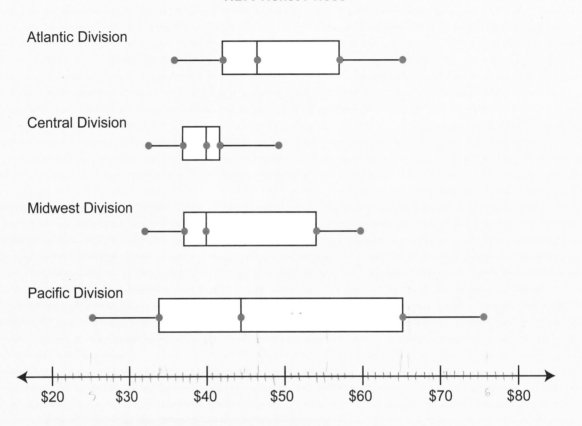

Using this information, answer the following:

a) For the Atlantic Division, estimate:

i) the minimum ticket prices;

ii) the lower quartile;

iii) the median;

iv) and upper quartile; and

v) the maximum.

b) For the Pacific Division, estimate:

    i) the minimum ticket prices;

    ii) the lower quartile;

    iii) the median;

    iv) the upper quartile; and

    v) the maximum.

c) Compare the prices of the four divisions using the information on the box-and-whisker plot.

For Questions 6 and 7, use the data found in Question 5.

6. a) The median is in the far right of the box for the Central Division. What does this tell you about that data set?

    b) The median is in the far left of the box for the Midwest Division. What does this tell you about that data set?

7. The Central Division has a shorter box, while the Pacific Division has long box. What does this tell you about the set of prices within each box?

8. Explain what an interquartile range is. What does this number tell you about the data?

9. By looking at the plots in Question 5, do you think any values could be outliers? If so, check by finding the interquartile range and calculating.

10. Mr. Marolda (from page 48) had a student, Marcos, who was absent when his math test was given. When Marcos took the make-up test, his score was a 38.

    a) Include this new piece of data and find the five-number summary.

    b) Is Marcos's score an outlier? Explain your answer mathematically.

11. Tina's older sister wants to buy a used car. She loves convertibles, and in the online classified section of her local newspaper, there were 11 listings. The asking prices were $14,995, $9,990, $13,995, $5,499, $9,995, $7,900, $9,990, $6,988, $12,995, $9,495 and $8,995.

Another online auction site showed 13 used convertibles for sale. The asking prices were $15,988, $12,995, $7,800, $7,200, $3,000, $9,995, $8,900, $7,500, $7,000, $19,995, $4,959, $5,357 and $13,800. She wondered which site overall had the better deals.

a) Find a five-number summary for each set of data.

b) Create a box-and-whisker plot comparing the two sets.

c) Would you expect any value to be an outlier? Why or why not? Check your prediction.

d) Give some reasons why the prices vary.

e) If Tina's sister wanted to find cheaper cars, on which of these sites should she keep looking? Explain.

f) If Tina's sister wanted to find a wider range of prices, on which of these sites should she keep looking? Explain.

12. For each of the following data displays, tell whether or not you can find the measures listed using the display.

Type of Display	Mean	Median	Mode	Range	Minimum	Maximum	Distribution of the Data (gaps, clusters, spread)	Outliers
Histogram								
Line Plot								
Stem-and-Leaf Plot								
Box-and-Whisker Plot								

13. Tyron, Jesse, Antonio and Kylee made the following table for the number of tickets they sold for the school dance.

Name	Tyron	Jesse	Antonio	Kylee
Number of Tickets	18	13	22	12
Percent	28%	20%	34%	18%

They want to make a graph to display their information as parts of a whole. Which would be the best type of graph for them to use?

A. Line graph   C. Stem-and-leaf plot

B. Box plot   D. Circle graph

14. Describe a situation where:

a) using a circle graph would be most helpful;

b) using a histogram would be most helpful;

c) using a line plot would be most helpful;

d) using a box-and-whisker plot would be most helpful.

 Think Beyond

15. Create a set of realistic data about a situation where there are outliers below the minimum and above the maximum. Prove that you have outliers. Create a box-and-whisker plot showing the outliers.

 Hint
See page 121

Think Back

16. Luke, Jett, Cole and Ben have dinner together. The bill comes to $44.00 and they plan to leave a 15% tip. If they divide the bill and tip evenly, how much should each one pay?

17. Which of the following is *not* equivalent to the expression $|5 - 8|$?

    A. $|8 - 5|$ **C.** $-(5 - 8)$

    B. $8 - 5$ **D.** $(5 - 8)$

18. Manon made the following table of a linear relationship.

x	0	1		5		25	50
y	5	7	9	15	25		105

    Write the equation and fill in the rest of the boxes.

19. Marika's bike tires have a radius of 13". If she rides a 3-mile route, how many rotations will each tire make? (Use 3.14 for π.)

20. **a)** Without multiplying it out, what is the final value of $(-10)^{13}$?

    b) How does that compare to $(-10)^{12}$?

    c) How does $(-10)^{13}$ compare to -10^{12}?

    d) Why are the answers different?

Optional Technology Lesson for this section available in your eBook

Sum It Up

In this section, you reviewed different types of data displays (circle graph, bar graph, histogram, table) and how each one can help you tell the story of a data set. You learned how to choose the most appropriate representation for a given data set. You learned how to use a stem-and-leaf plot to organize data. You learned how to create a box-and-whisker plot to display data. You compared data sets using bar graphs and box-and-whisker plots.

The important ideas in this section include the following:

Displaying Categorical Data

■ Categorical data have specific labels and can be categorized or put into groups (for example, favorite food, birthday month, eye color).

■ To display categorical data, we most often use a circle graph or bar graph.

A **circle graph** is useful to show percents or parts of a single whole.

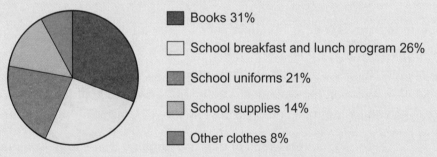

■ Books 31%

□ School breakfast and lunch program 26%

■ School uniforms 21%

□ School supplies 14%

■ Other clothes 8%

A **bar graph** is useful for showing actual numbers of occurrences. A bar graph is also useful for comparing the amounts in the same category between two or more different data sets.

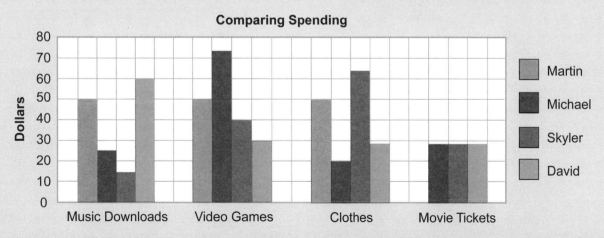

Displaying Numerical Data

■ Numerical data have assigned number values (for example, age, test score, temperature, distance, time).

■ To display numerical data, we most often use a line plot, a stem-and-leaf plot, a box-and-whisker plot or a histogram. You can also use a circle graph or bar graph if there are a small number of groups that data values can be placed in. For numerical data that can be grouped into intervals, you can use a histogram to show frequencies.

A **line plot** is useful for finding the median and the mode. You can calculate the mean using the information displayed on a line plot. This display also shows gaps and clusters in the data.

Number of Points Scored in a Basketball Game

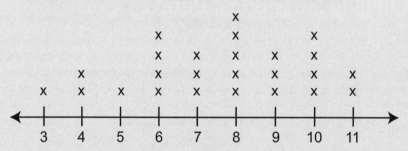

A **histogram** is used with numerical data that are grouped into intervals (for example, temperatures in the 60s, the 70s, the 80s and the 90s, or ages 0–9, 10–19, 20–29, 30–39). The bars indicate the frequency of the values over each specified interval. The intervals all have equal widths, and the bars touch each other. In the case of the histogram shown, one interval has no values, and that is represented by the darkened line segment on the x-axis.

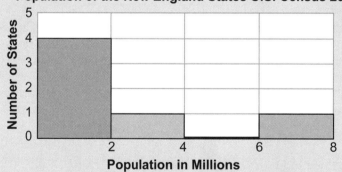

Population of the New England States U.S. Census 2000

In order to find a median, you need to organize data from least to greatest. A **stem-and-leaf plot** is useful for organizing data sets. This is necessary to find the median. You can easily identify the median and the mode from a stem-and-leaf plot and can calculate the mean using information displayed on this plot. You need to identify what the stem and leaf represent in a key.

Ms. Spinelli's Class Grades

7	1 2 6 7 8 8
8	2 4 4 5 6 7 8 9
9	1 2 3 4 5 7

Key: 7 | 1 = 71

To display data using the median, you can use a **box-and-whisker plot (box plot)**. This is especially useful when comparing two or more large data sets. To create a box-and-whisker plot, you need to find the five-number summary.

Comparing Test Scores

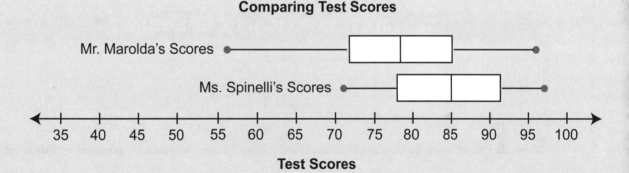

Test Scores

- The **five-number summary** includes the minimum value and the maximum value. It also includes the median. Finally, the summary includes Q1, the lower quartile (the median of the scores below the median of the entire data set) and Q3, the upper quartile (the median of the scores above the median of the data set). The five-number summary is generally written in order of increasing value: the minimum, Q1, the median (Q2), Q3, and the maximum.

- **Outliers** are data values that are far from the median. They are calculated using the **interquartile range** (Q3 – Q1). To see if a data value is an outlier, multiply the interquartile range by 1.5 and:

  1. Add this product to Q3. Any data values above your answer are outliers; and,

  2. Subtract this product from Q1. Any data values below your answer are outliers.

■ You can use your graphing calculator to create box-and-whisker plots. On some calculators, if there is an outlier, the whisker in the direction of the outlier will end at the data value right before the outlier. The outlier will be marked as a point on the graph.

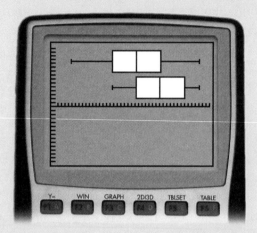

MATHEMATICALLY SPEAKING

Do you know what these mathematical terms mean?

▶ box-and-whisker plot (box plot)   ▶ five-number summary   ▶ numerical data

▶ categorical data   ▶ histogram   ▶ outliers

▶ first or lower quartile, Q1   ▶ interquartile range   ▶ third or upper quartile, Q3

Part 1. What did you learn?

1. Emma and Frankie asked their classmates how many movies they see each year. They organized their data in the histogram below.

   a. Did Emma and Frankie collect categorical or numerical data?

   b. Do you think a histogram is an appropriate data display for the data? Why or why not?

   c. Write three conclusions about the data.

Movies Seen at a Movie Theater

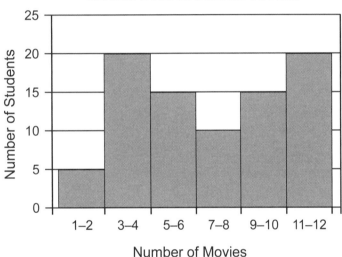

2. Finn and Nicole asked their classmates how long (in minutes) it takes them to travel to school each morning. They organized their data in the box-and-whisker plot below.

   a. Did Finn and Nicole collect categorical or numerical data?

   b. Estimate the five-number summary of their data set.

   c. Write three conclusions about the data.

Travel Time (in minutes) to School

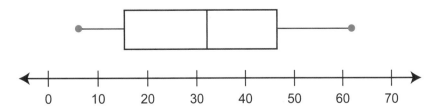

3. Inacio, Meg and Theo each asked students in their homerooms whether they preferred listening to music on the radio, a CD player or an MP3 player. Each student organized his or her data in a circle graph and reported one conclusion about the data. Match each conclusion on the left with the correct circle graph on the right.

Conclusion	Circle Graph
a. The number of people who prefer listening to music on their MP3 players is about twice the number who prefer the radio.	**i.** 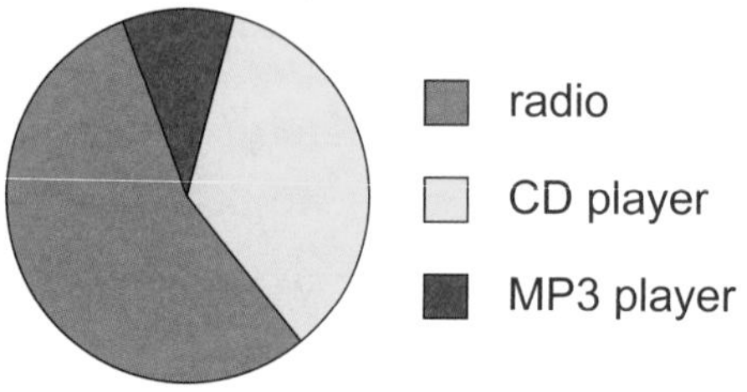 radio / CD player / MP3 player
b. About $\frac{1}{3}$ of the people I surveyed prefer listening to music on a CD player.	**ii.** 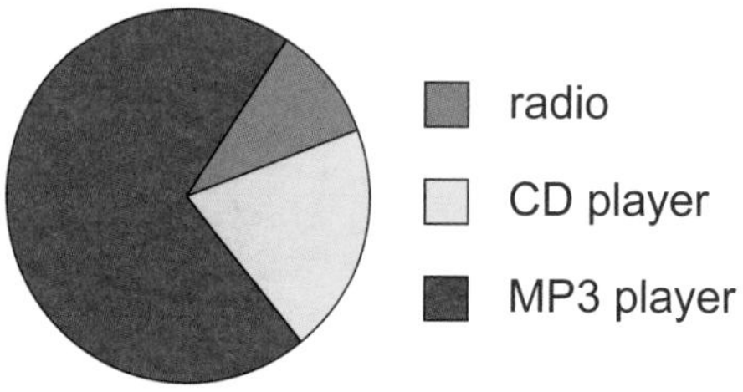 radio / CD player / MP3 player
c. Almost 75% of the people I surveyed prefer listening to music on their MP3 players.	**iii.** 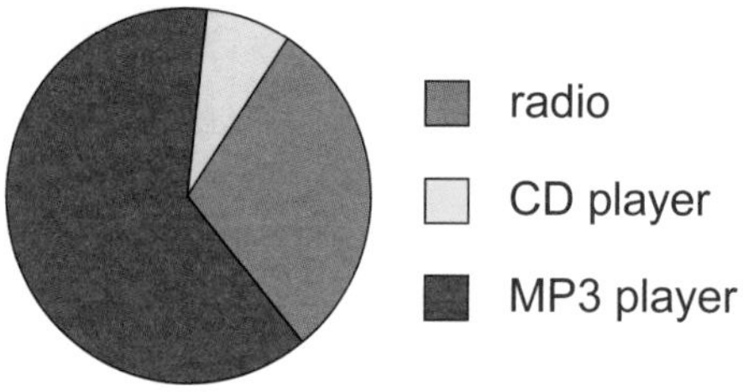 radio / CD player / MP3 player

4. Daron surveyed 29 teachers in his school to find out how many years they have been teaching at his school. Daron's data set is below.

1, 1, 1, 2, 2, 2, 3, 3, 3, 3, 4, 5, 5, 5, 5, 8, 8, 9, 9, 9, 10, 10, 12, 13, 14, 17, 17, 20, 25

a. Find the five-number summary of the data set.

b. Calculate the interquartile range.

c. Use the interquartile range to identify any outliers.

d. Create box-and-whisker plot of the data.

e. Use your box-and-whisker plot to write three conclusions about the data set.

5. Daron wants to display his data in another type of graph. Explain whether each choice below is an appropriate way to display Daron's data.

   a. bar graph

   b. histogram

   c. stem-and-leaf plot

   d. circle graph

Part 2. What Went Wrong?

6. Clarissa's teacher asked her to identify the trends in the data organized in the box-and-whisker plot below.

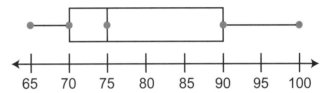

   Clarissa said, "There are no trends in the data. It looks like the data are evenly spread out from 65 to 100." What doesn't Clarissa understand about box-and-whisker plots? What could you say or do to help Clarissa use the plot to find trends in the data?

7. Hank surveyed his classmates about the number of minutes they spend brushing their teeth each day. He found the five-number summary of the data he collected.

   His teacher told him that he found the minimum, median and maximum values correctly. But he said that his lower quartile and upper quartiles were not correct. What did Hank do wrong? What are the lower and upper quartiles of Hank's data set?

8. Haddie surveyed 40 classmates about the number of songs they had on their MP3 players. She organized the data in the stem-and-leaf plot below.

2	0	1	5	5	6	
3	4	5	6	9		
4	5	5	8			
5	0	1	3	6	9	9
6	5	7	8	8		
7	0	0	4			
8	0	2	4	6	8	8
9	1	2	5	5	6	7
10	0	5	5			

She found that the median value in her data set was 67.5. But she said, "That can't be right. There is no such thing as half of a song!" How would you respond to Haddie? Has she calculated the median correctly? If so, how should she interpret the value of 67.5?

In Search of a Relationship

Statisticians often look for a relationship between two variables in a data set. If they find one, they use this information to create mathematical models that make predictions. For example, statisticians use models to predict the performance of the stock market, to predict the effectiveness of prescription drugs, and to predict the number of teenage driver car accidents in order to set insurance rates. The uses of mathematics are far-reaching and important!

 Are the Variables Related?

Graph the following set of data on coordinate axes with number of calories on the *x*-axis and number of carbohydrates on the *y*-axis.

Type of Fruit Smoothie	Number of Calories	Number of Carbohydrates in Grams
Melon Blast	65	17
Strawberry Ice	63	15.5
Cranberry Cooler	60	8.5
Coconut Crush	70	18
Gonzilla Grape	118	48
Arctic Cherry	40	8.5
Plum Pudding	65	27
Colossal Kiwi	55	15
Banana Split	70	17

1. Did you connect the points? Why or why not?

2. How is this set of data different from those sets you've used to create line plots or box-and-whisker plots?

In this lesson you will take on the role of statistician for a travel magazine, *On the Go*. You will investigate trends in data for three different topics. First, the magazine has taken a survey to learn about spending patterns of different age groups while on a cruise. People were asked how much money per day they were planning to spend on extras not included in the cruise line's fees. Readers will find this information useful in planning their own vacation cruises. Cruise lines will find it useful in deciding what type of extra excursions to offer and what type and number of items to stock in their gift stores.

Take a look at the table that lists ages of people and their spending allowance per day.

1. a) Do you notice any connection or relationship between age and spending allowance?

b) What type of graph might you use to show relationships between two variables?

Cruise Vacation Spending Patterns Based on Age

Age (years)	Spending Allowance Per Day (dollars)
20	$130
25	$132
30	$140
35	$144
40	$148
45	$150
50	$152
55	$155

A good choice for the graph would be a scatter plot.

 **Let's Review**   A **scatter plot** is a graph that shows the relationship between two variables on coordinate axes. The points in a scatter plot are distinct, and so they are not connected.

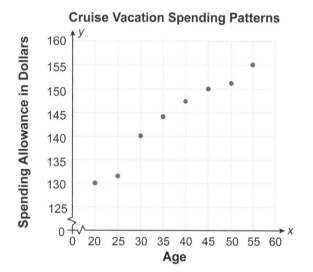

Two variables that are related are said to have a **correlation** between them. You can easily see from the graph that as age increases, the amount of money people are planning to take also increases. In fact, we can almost draw a straight line connecting the points. Statisticians would say that this shows a **positive correlation** between age and spending allowance since as one variable increases, so does the other.

If we could draw one straight line that passed through every point, this would be a linear function and have a **perfect correlation**. In a perfect correlation, the two variables are related to each other in exactly the same way for every ordered pair.

2. Below is a scatter plot showing the average spending per day for 25 people aged 20 to 55 years on one of Festival Cruise Line's trips to Bermuda. Do you notice any trends in this data?

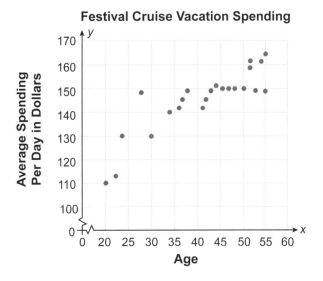

Festival Cruise Vacation Spending

If we tried to connect the points in this graph, they would not be as close to one straight line as in the previous plot. However, we can still say that spending is positively correlated with age since the trend shows that, in general, as age increases so does the amount spent. This graph shows a strong (but not perfect) positive correlation between age and money spent.

NOTE We cannot say that getting older *causes* people to spend more money or plan to spend more money on a cruise. There may be many factors that determine how much money people plan to spend or actually do spend, such as income level, types of food and drink they wish to purchase, kinds of activities they enjoy, and so on. When there is a correlation between variables, all you can state is that there is a relationship between the two variables, that is, a general trend. But a relationship does *not* imply a cause-and-effect situation.

---

3. Write a paragraph that summarizes your findings for *On the Go*. Share with a partner and then with the class.

There are other types of relationships between variables. If one variable tends to decrease as the other increases, this is a negative correlation. The following graph shows a negative correlation. In general, as the x-values increase, the y-values decrease.

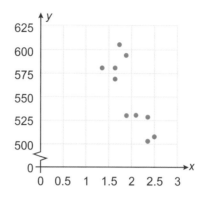

Some variables are not correlated at all and show no graphical patterns. The next graph shows two variables that have *no correlation*. There is no pattern or general trend.

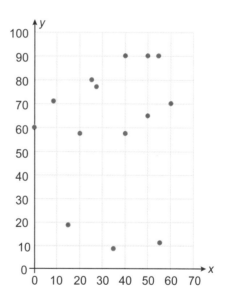

Snacks on Vacation

In their next teen issue, *On the Go* will feature an article on advice about snacks in their "Healthy Travel Tips" column. You are hired to see if there is a relationship between the number of calories and the number of grams of carbohydrates in different types of fruit smoothies.

4. Examine the scatter plot you made in the Start It Off. Does there appear to be a correlation between the two variables? Explain your answer.

5. Write a paragraph reporting your results and their implications for healthy snacking for the "Healthy Travel Tips" column.

Next, you are asked to conduct an analysis of attendance at the Newton Discovery Center based on weather and time of year. *On the Go* will publish your findings in an article so readers can decide when would be the best time of year to make a visit.

6. First, predict whether or not there is a correlation between temperature and attendance and between rainfall and attendance. What type of correlation would you predict in each case?

7. Following are data that you have gathered. Create four scatter plots to determine if any correlations exist between the temperature or rainfall and attendance for that month. Work in groups of four with each member making one scatter plot using one set of data. Use your graphing calculator.

Temps in April (°F)	Attendance	Temps in July (°F)	Attendance
63	1,349	62	843
64	1,460	84	3,851
54	755	82	3,461
58	832	75	2,315
50	700	60	732
71	1,700	92	1,456
75	2,001	90	1,657
61	1,024	83	3,387
57	801	81	2,974
62	650	77	1,574

Rainfall in May (inches)	Attendance	Rainfall in August (inches)	Attendance
0	2,004	0	3,856
0.5	1,500	0.1	3,651
0.2	1,874	0.4	2,056
0.7	321	0.8	954
1	53	0.2	2,456
1.2	21	0	3,967
0.01	2,546	0.5	1,543
0	2,500	0	3,777
0.3	1,264	0.7	1,022
0.01	1,742	0.4	1,543

 **Let's Review** You used your TI84+ graphing calculator to create scatter plots in *Line it Up: Exploring Linear Relationships*. Here is a quick review.

Step 1 Go to **[STAT]** and **[EDIT]**. Enter the data in **[L1]** (*x*-values) and **[L2]** (*y*-values).

Step 2 Go to **[STAT PLOT]** and make sure plot is **[ON]**. Choose the scatter plot graph.

Step 3 Go to **[WINDOW]** and set your window so that all the values will be graphed. Check maximum and minimum values and scales for both *x*- and *y*-axes.

Step 4 Press **[GRAPH]**.

8. Interpret the data with your group.

a) Does there appear to be any correlation between temperature and attendance? If so, what type?

b) Does this correlation vary between the spring and the summer? Why might this be the case?

c) Does there appear to be a correlation between amount of rainfall and attendance? If so, what type?

d) Does this correlation vary between the spring and the summer? Why might this be the case?

9. Write a summary report for the editors to include in the *On the Go* article. Discuss the correlations you found. Try to explain any variations in the data. For example, why might attendance have varied on days with the same temperature or rainfall?

 **Hint**
See page 121

10. Based on your statistics, why might a reader choose to go to the Discovery Center on a rainy day in August or a 95° day in July?

Like Oil and Water

There are situations when no correlation or relationship exists between variables. Can you think of a situation where this might happen in the real world?

11. Talk to your partner and come up with two variables that have no connection, that is, when one increases or decreases the other does not follow an increasing or decreasing pattern. Predict what the scatter plot might look like. Discuss your examples with the class.

12. Below is a table of the number of people who rode the Space Explorer ride at the Discovery Center on Tuesdays and Thursdays in August.

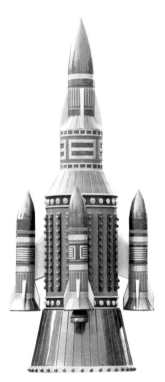

Number of Space Explorer Riders on Tuesdays and Thursdays in August	
August Date	Number of Riders
3	1,025
5	346
10	845
12	1,187
17	41
19	435
24	0
26	885
31	199

a) Do you think there is a correlation between these two variables? Explain.

b) Draw a scatter plot. Make sure the values on the x-axis are evenly spaced from 1 to 31.

c) Was your prediction correct?

d) Analyze and discuss the graph you have created. Why might the number of riders vary so greatly?

e) What might be a reason that nobody went on the ride on August 24?

13. Discuss with your partner whether or not there is a positive, negative or no correlation between each pair of variables listed. Then share with the class.

a) The height and weight of a man

b) The amount of sunshine and size of a puddle

c) The temperature and the sale of ice cream cones

d) Hair color and hat size

e) The amount of advertising and attendance at a play

f) The temperature and amount of sand at the beach

Wrap It Up

Discuss with a partner how a scatter plot is used to indicate a possible correlation between two variables. How is a positive correlation different from a negative correlation? How can you tell if two variables are not related at all?

MATHEMATICALLY SPEAKING

▶ correlation

▶ negative correlation

▶ perfect correlation

▶ positive correlation

▶ scatter plot

Write About It

1. **a)** How are the data we analyzed in this lesson different from the data we analyzed in Sections 1 and 2?

    b) Can you use a circle graph, bar graph or box-and-whisker plot to analyze these data? Why or why not?

     **Hint**
    See page 121

2. Make up a set of data showing a positive correlation between the number of hours you study for a math test and the grade you receive on the test, expressed as a percent. Show the data in a table and on a scatter plot. (Do not create a perfect correlation!)

3. **a)** Describe a situation in which a statistician at a pharmaceutical company would determine the correlation between two variables. Name the variables.

    b) Describe a situation in which a statistician at the U.S. Department of Education would determine the correlation between two variables. Name the variables.

4. Describe a situation in which there would be no correlation between two variables. Name the variables and explain your reasoning.

5. State whether each scatter plot implies a positive, negative or no correlation.

    a)
    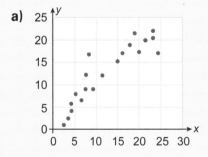

    b)
    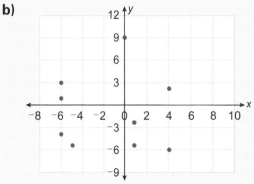

c)

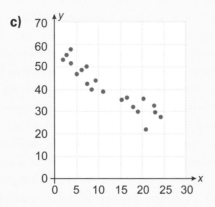

d)

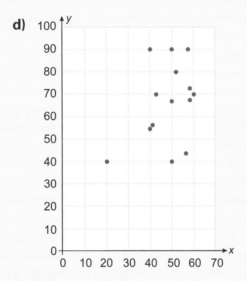

6. Predict whether there is a positive, negative or no correlation between the two variables listed.

   a) Length of a side of a square and the area of the square

   b) The price of a gallon of gas and the number of bicycles purchased in the same area

   c) Grade on an algebra exam and the number of minutes it takes a student to run a mile in gym class

   d) The price of summer clothing and the amount purchased by customers

   e) The number of mosquitoes and the amount of spring rainfall

7. Choose one of the situations above to demonstrate the fact that correlation does not by itself mean that the change in one variable is necessarily *causing* the change in the other variable.

Think Beyond

8. A perfect correlation is assigned the value of +1 for a perfect positive correlation and −1 for a perfect negative correlation. If there is no correlation, the value is 0. Research how statisticians calculate the correlation coefficient, *r*. Find the correlation between age and spending allowance in the table at the start of this lesson. You may want to use the tutorial on the following website to help you.
www.easycalculation.com/statistics/learn-correlation.php

Think Back

9. Given the equation $y = 2 - \frac{1}{2}x$,

   a) When graphed on an *x-y* coordinate plane, will the function increase or decrease?

   b) Find the slope and the *y*-intercept of the line.

   c) Write the equation for a line parallel to this line with a *y*-intercept at $y = -3$.

10. If Elleree has a four-color spinner where every color is equal in size, what is the probability that she will spin the same color twice in a row (with only two spins)?

11. A rectangular piece of paper measures 11" × 14". To the nearest inch, estimate the length of its diagonal.

12. What value is halfway between −5.4 and 2.7 on the number line?

13. Morgan drew a line segment from the point (3, 4) to the point (7, 4). If Morgan wants to make a right triangle with an area of 8, what is a possible coordinate for the third point? What are some other possible coordinates for the third point?

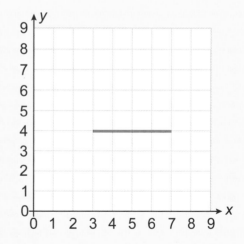

3.2 The Best Fit

➡ Start It Off

Ladybugs are taking over the world! It started with one cute bug on my windowsill, but each day the number of ladybugs increased by 3.

1. How many ladybugs were there after 3 days? After 5 days? After 10 days? (Assume none of the babies will create more ladybugs.)

2. Make a graph using a coordinate grid with time on the *x*-axis and the number of ladybugs on the *y*-axis.

3. What shape is the graph? What does this mean about the rate of growth?

4. What is the coordinate where this line crosses the *y*-axis?

5. What is the slope of this line? What is the meaning of slope in terms of the number of ladybugs?

How Tall Are Your Classmates?

Are you good at approximating the height of a person? In this activity, you will approximate the heights of students and some adults and then compare this to their actual height in centimeters.

1. a) With a partner, use a table like the one below to record your data. Write the names of the students in your class in the first column. Also include the names of your teacher and two other adults who have volunteered to participate. These might be your principal, your school nurse, your custodian or another teacher.

Approximating Heights

Name	Actual Height x-Coordinate (cm)	Approximated Height y-Coordinate (cm)	Ordered Pair (x, y)

    b) First you will establish benchmarks. Have two students stand in front of the classroom as each set of partners approximates their height in centimeters. Then measure the actual height and record in centimeters to the nearest centimeter. The two students then return to their seats.

    c) Next, in groups of five, students will come to the front of the room and you and your partner will approximate each student's height to the nearest centimeter and write the approximations down in column 3.

    d) Once the heights of the entire class and adults have all been approximated, in pairs measure each other's height and record the actual heights. Share the measurements with the class so everyone can fill in column 2.

2. a) From your table, create a scatter plot of points whose coordinates are (actual height, approximated height). Decide on appropriate scales for each axis. Discuss this with your partner and then decide as a class. Use the same scales for both the x- and y-axes.

    b) Would you say there is a correlation between the approximations and actual heights on your scatter plot?

3. Look at the point that represents your teacher's height. What do the coordinates of this point represent?

4. a) Did you approximate the correct height at least once? If so, describe the location of the point(s) on the scatter plot.

    b) Did you underestimate the height of someone at least once? If so, describe the location of the point(s) on the scatter plot.

    c) Did you overestimate the height of someone at least once? If so, describe the location of the point(s) on the scatter plot.

5. Put a circle around any points that are far from the main clusters of points.

6. Overall, did you make reasonable and consistent approximations? How can you tell from your scatter plot?

The Perfect Guesser

7. Suppose you had approximated every person's height correctly. Predict what your scatter plot would look like.

8. Use a different color to circle the points where your approximations were correct. If you connected these circled points, would they form a line?

9. Describe the points on the line formed when approximated heights equal exact heights based on their distances from the x- and y-axes. Write a description of this linear function in words and then using an equation. Compare your equation with your classmates'. Did you all get the same equation?

10. Where does a point with an underestimate of the height lie in relation to this line? What about a point where the approximation is higher than the actual value?

In this case, the line $y = x$ can be used as a benchmark to determine the strength of the relationship between approximated and actual height. Points on this line show a perfect correlation between the approximated and actual heights. As you have learned, two variables are considered to be correlated if there is a strong general trend that connects them. In this situation, the closer the points are to the line $y = x$, the stronger the trend and the greater the correlation between approximated and actual heights.

11. How close are your data to the line $y = x$?

The Best Fit

MATHEMATICALLY SPEAKING

▶ line of best fit

To describe the relationship between two variables and to predict other values in the data set, statisticians find an equation that relates the two variables. For data that show a linear pattern, they use a line of best fit. In general, approximately half the points in the data set will fall above this line and about half the points will fall below the line. Some points will be close to or on the line.

One possible graph of the actual heights of students compared to approximations of their heights is shown. A line of best fit has been drawn. You can see that five points lie on the line, three points are just above the line and four points are below the line.

12. a) What is the equation of this line?

b) How did you find this equation?

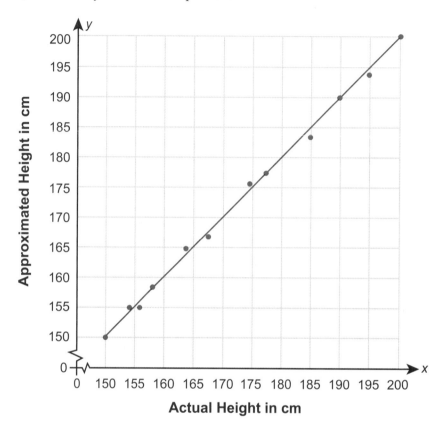

Actual Height in cm

Finding a Line of Best Fit

One way to find a line of best fit is to try placing different lines to see which one has approximately half the data points above and half the data points below the line.

13. Take a piece of thin uncooked spaghetti and place it on your scatter plot. The spaghetti represents a line. Move the line until you find a place where the line seems to go through the middle of all your data points so that, of all the points not on the line, about half are above and about half are below it.

a) Draw this line on your graph.

b) Write the equation of your line of best fit.

Let's Review

To write the equation of your line of best fit, first find the slope of the line using slope triangles. Then find the *y*-intercept, the point where the line crosses the *y*-axis. Now you can write the slope-intercept form of the line, $y = mx + b$, where *m* is the slope and *b* is the *y*-intercept.

   c) Compare equations with your classmates. Do any students have equations different from the line $y = x$? How many different equations were found? Why might they be different?

14. a) Find two more points on your line of best fit.

   b) What do the values of the *x*- and *y*-coordinates mean in terms of the height of a person?

   c) Given the actual height of a student, is your line a good predictor of a guessed height?

MATHEMATICALLY SPEAKING

▶ line of best fit

Explain what a line of best fit is and how it helps tell the story about a data set.

Write
About It

1. Explain how statisticians use linear functions to approximate real-life situations. Use the terms *scatter plot*, *linear functions*, *line of best fit* and *correlation* in your explanation.

2. Look at the line that represents actual heights equaling approximated heights ($y = x$). Where would a point lie that shows an approximation that is 7 centimeters shorter than the actual height? Write the equation of the line that represents approximations that are consistently 7 centimeters shorter than the actual heights. In mathematical terms, what does the 7 represent?

3. **a)** Why do you know for certain that the point (0, 0) will *not* be plotted on the scatter plot for approximated height compared to actual height?

   b) Could it be on a line of best fit? Explain.

4. For each scatter plot below, tell whether or not you think the line drawn is a good fit for the data. Explain your reasoning.

   a)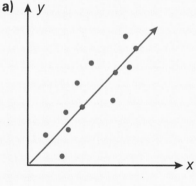

   c)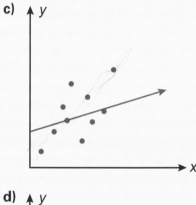

   b)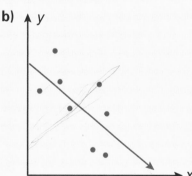

   d)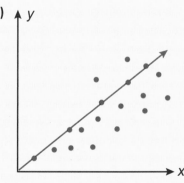

5. In the last lesson, we found that the scatter plot below showed a positive correlation between age and spending patterns on a cruise.

a) Using a piece of spaghetti to help you, draw a line of best fit on the scatter plot. Explain why it is a good fit for the data.

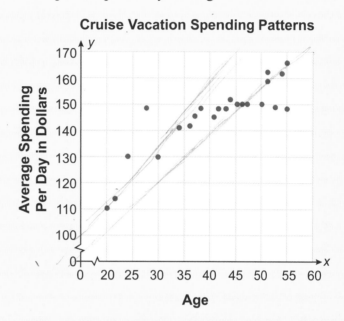

Cruise Vacation Spending Patterns

b) Use your line of best fit to predict the spending patterns per day of a cruise-goer who is 60 years old.

6. Look at the scatter plots below. In some cases the data have a relationship and in other cases they do not.

   a) Predict whether or not the variables are correlated and what type of correlation exists (positive or negative).

   b) If it looks like there is a correlation, find a line of best fit and write the equation for the line.

   c) Explain why it is a line of best fit.

   i.

   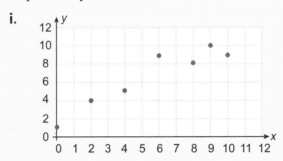

   ii.

   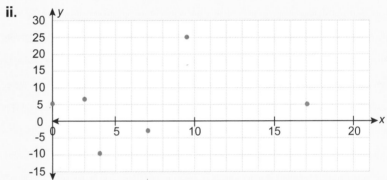

   iii.

   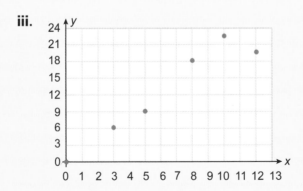

7. Klaudio said he could draw a line of best fit for, Graph ii of Question 6 that would have three points above it and three points below it. Rafael agreed that you could draw this line, but it really did not serve as a line of best fit for these data. Explain what Rafael meant.

    **Hint**
   See page 121

8. Dishonda thinks that a good line of best fit for Question 6c, Graph i would be $y = 6$. Do you agree? Explain your reasoning.

9. For the *On the Go* magazine "Healthy Travel Tips" column, you have been asked to compare the number of calories to the number of grams of fat in each candy listed in the table below. The serving size of each candy listed is approximately the same.

Analyzing Calories and Fat in Popular Candy

Name of Candy	Number of Calories	Number of Grams of Fat
Reese's Pieces®	210	10
Raisinets®	190	8
Milk Duds®	170	6
M&Ms®	240	10
Junior Mints®	170	3
Swedish Fish®	160	0
Whoppers®	190	7
Hershey's Kisses®	230	14
Twizzlers®	140	1
Skittles®	250	2.5
Tootsie Roll®	140	3
Starburst®	240	5
Rolo®	190	8
Good & Plenty®	160	0

http://www.acaloriecounter.com/candy-chocolate.php

a) Create a scatter plot of the data and predict whether or not there is a correlation. If there is one, describe the correlation as positive or negative.

b) Draw a line of best fit on your graph.

c) Find an equation for this line using slope and *y*-intercept.

Think Beyond

10. Write a paragraph for the "Healthy Travel Tips" column describing your findings from Question 9 and offer some nutritional tips based on your findings.

11. Use your line of best fit on your graph from Question 9 to predict the number of grams of fat in a candy bar that has 260 calories.

Think Beyond

12. a) Use your equation from Question 9 to predict the number of grams of fat in a candy bar that has 260 calories.

b) Compare the results using your line to the results using your equation. Explain why they might be different answers.

Think Back

13. If 7 bushels of corn are worth $49.00, what are 3 bushels of the same type of corn worth? Write a general equation to calculate the cost of any number of bushels.

14. A triangle has angles A, B and C. The sum of the angle measures in a triangle is 180°. If the measure of angle B is 2 times that of angle C, and the measure of angle A is 3 times that of angle C, what is the measure of each angle?

15. Given the equation $y = 2x - 13$, solve for y when $x = {}^-3$.

16. In 1954, Roger Bannister was the first man to run a 4-minute mile. How many feet per second is that?

17. Sonya had 24 pieces of fruit. She gave $\frac{3}{8}$ of the fruit to Erol, $\frac{1}{6}$ of the fruit to Erin, kept 1 piece for herself and gave the rest to Kerim. How many pieces did Kerim get? What portion of the fruit did Kerim get? Express this as a fraction in lowest terms.

Using Statistics to Find the Best Fit

➡ Start It Off

For my birthday, my uncle gave me a bug container with 5 bugs that do not reproduce, plus 1 ladybug that has 3 new babies every day.

1. How many total bugs do I have after 3 days? After 5 days? After 10 days? (Assume the babies cannot reproduce.)

2. Write a formula for the total number of bugs after x days.

3. Graph this data on the same grid that you used for the Start It Off in Lesson 3.2.

4. How are the two graphs similar? How are they different? How do the parts of your formula match the graph?

Using the Mean

You can use statistical procedures to find a more precise line of best fit than we did in the previous lesson. Let's use the data on the amount of calories and carbohydrates found in fruit drinks to investigate this.

Type of Fruit Smoothie	Number of Calories	Number of Carbohydrates (in grams)
Melon Blast	65	17
Strawberry Ice	63	15.5
Cranberry Cooler	60	8.5
Coconut Crush	70	18
Gonzilla Grape	118	48
Arctic Cherry	40	8.5
Plum Pudding	65	27
Colossal Kiwi	55	15
Banana Split	70	17

You created a scatter plot of these data in the Start It Off for Lesson 3.1. It should resemble the one below.

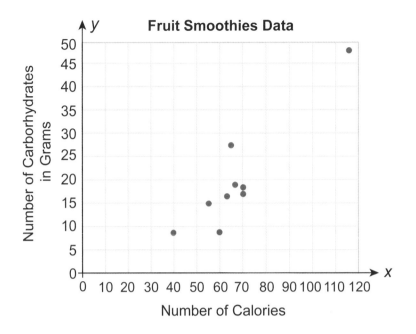

Follow these steps to find a line of best fit using the mean.

Step 1 Find the mean number of calories and the mean number of carbohydrates from the data table.

Step 2 Plot a point on the graph with the mean calories as the *x*-value and mean carbohydrates as the *y*-value.

Step 3 Draw a line through your plotted mean point that could be a line of best fit. Remember to have about the same number of points above the line as below the line.

1. Using the graph of your line of best fit, predict how many carbohydrates a fruit smoothie with 80 calories might have.

2. Using the graph of your line of best fit, predict how many calories a fruit smoothie that contains 20 grams of carbohydrates might have.

3. One equation for the relationship between number of calories and number of grams of carbohydrates that goes through the mean is $y = 1.043x - 50.83$.

   a) Show that this line contains the point (mean calories, mean carbohydrates).

   b) Use this equation to find the number of carbohydrates in the Melon Blast. Does it come close to the actual data? Explain your answer.

Using Box-and-Whisker Plots

You can also use box-and-whisker plots to find a line of best fit. The data below are taken from an international study called the Trends in International Mathematics and Science Study (TIMSS). It is conducted every few years to compare student achievement in mathematics and science in different countries. The table shows the average number of hours an eighth-grade student in a particular country meets or talks with friends during the course of a day and that student's average score on the math test. Singapore students came in first in the world on this test!

Country	No. of Hours Meeting or Talking with Friends	Mathematics Test Score
Singapore	1.7	605
Korea	1.8	589
Hong Kong	1.6	586
Chinese Taipei	1.4	585
Japan	1.6	570
Belgium	1.9	537
Netherlands	2.0	536
Hungary	2.2	529
Malaysia	1.5	508
Latvia	2.8	508
Russian Federation	2.5	508
Australia	1.7	504
United States	2.4	502

Below is a scatter plot for the data.

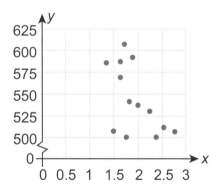

4. Add labels to the axes and give the graph a title.

5. Find the data points for Singapore and the United States. Are you surprised by any of the data given? If so, explain.

6. We will now determine a line of best fit using box-and-whisker plots. Use the top graph on Lesson Guide 3.3: *Using Box-and-Whisker Plots* to plot your data.

Step 1 Find the five-number summary for the data given for the number of hours spent meeting or talking with friends. Make a box-and-whisker plot for these data just below the *x*-axis, aligned with the numbers on the *x*-axis.

Step 2 Find the five-number summary for the data given for the mathematics test scores. Make a box-and-whisker plot for these data just to the left of the *y*-axis, aligned with the numbers on the *y*-axis so that it is positioned vertically.

Step 3 a. Draw vertical lines from the two *x*-values indicating the upper and lower quartiles on the box-and-whisker plot for the number of hours playing or talking with friends.

   b. Draw horizontal lines from the two *y*-values indicating the upper and lower quartiles on the box-and-whisker plot for the mathematics test scores.

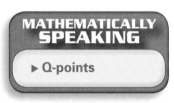

You now have a rectangle on your graph. The four points that form the vertices of this rectangle are called Q-points.

Step 4 Draw the diagonal inside this rectangle that shows the direction of the data. Extend the line beyond the rectangle.

Your graph should look like the one below.

Hours Teens Talk with a Friend Compared to Math Test Scores

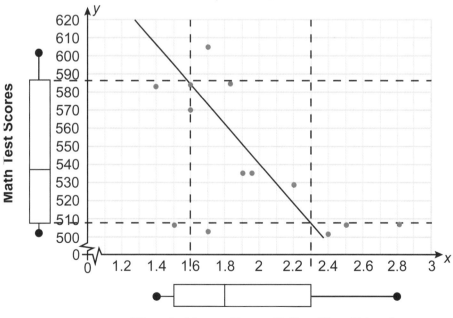

Time in Hours Teens Talk with a Friend

7. Name the coordinates of the Q-points.

8. Why is the line drawn in Step 4 considered a line of best fit?

9. Below is another set of data from the TIMSS international study.

   a) Draw a scatter plot on the bottom graph on Lesson Guide 3.3: *Using Box-and-Whisker Plots* and predict whether there is a correlation between the variables. If so, what type of correlation is it?

   b) Draw a line of best fit using box-and-whisker plots and Q-points following the steps above.

   c) Name the coordinates of the Q-points.

TIMSS Math Data

Country	No. of Hours Spent Each Day Playing Sports	Mathematics Test Score
Singapore	1.4	605
Korea	0.7	589
Hong Kong	1.0	586
Chinese Taipei	1.0	585
Japan	1.3	570
Belgium	1.6	537
Netherlands	1.7	536
Hungary	1.5	529
Malaysia	1.1	508
Latvia	1.3	508
Russian Federation	1.3	508
Australia	1.6	504
United States	1.8	502

10. Compare the line relating hours spent with friends to test scores and the line relating hours spent playing sports to test scores.

    a) How do the directions of the lines of best fit compare?

    b) How do the slopes of the lines compare in terms of steepness? What does this mean about the relationship of the variables?

Wrap It Up

MATHEMATICALLY
SPEAKING

▶ Q-points

What are the advantages and disadvantages of finding a line of best fit using the mean? The median and box-and-whisker plots? The "spaghetti method"?

Write About It

1. You have learned three different ways to create a line of best fit. Explain the three different methods. Be sure to include:

   a) Which method will result in everyone getting the same line?

   b) Which method will result in everyone having at least one point in common?

   c) Which is the quickest method?

2. Below are data about the temperatures in Death Valley, California.

Death Valley Temperatures

Month	Average High (°F)	Average Low (°F)
January	64.6	39.1
February	72.3	45.6
March	80.4	52.8
April	89.8	61.9
May	99.3	70.7
June	109.0	80.3
July	115.3	87.8
August	113.2	85.0
September	105.8	74.9
October	92.0	61.6
November	75.7	48.1
December	65.1	39.4

   a) Find the mean of both variables.

   b) Create a scatter plot of the data and plot the point that represents the mean of both variables.

   c) Draw a line of best fit through this point.

3. Refer to your graph from Question 2. If the high temperature is 120°, use the graph of your line to predict the low temperature.

4. Refer to your graph from Question 2. If the low temperature is 50°, use the graph of your line to predict the high temperature.

5. Following is a list of 10 NBA players, the average number of points per game that they scored in the 2007–2008 season and the number of years they have played in the NBA.

NBA Star Stats

Name of Player	Average Points per Game 2007–2008 Season	Year in NBA
Allen Iverson	26.4	12
Baron Davis	22.2	9
Michael Redd	22.7	8
Richard Jefferson	22.6	7
Chris Bosh	22.3	5
Yao Ming	22	6
Corey Maggette	22.1	9
Jason Richardson	21.8	7
Joe Johnson	21.7	7
Carlos Boozer	21.1	6

a) Using the five-number summary for each variable, create two box-and-whisker plots.

b) Create a scatter plot of the data.

c) Put the box-and-whisker plots on the scatter plot and find the Q-points.

d) Draw the line of best fit.

6. Dirk Nowitzki has played in the NBA for ten years. Use your line of best fit from Question 5 to predict the number of points that he scored during 2007–2008. Look up his actual record. Were you close? If not, can you give a reason?

7. Carmelo Anthony has played in the NBA for five years. Use your line of best fit from Question 5 to predict the number of points that he scored during the 2007–2008 season. Look up his actual record. Were you close? If not, can you give a reason?

8. Refer to your graph from Question 5. Give some reasons why a player may score less than a line of best fit would predict in a given year. Give some reasons why a player may score more than a line of best fit would predict in a given year.

Photo © Larry W. Smith/epa/Corbis

9. Are the Q-points always part of the data set? Why or why not?

10. Remember the bugs from the Start It Off? This time I have one little bug who adds 3 babies every day and one big bug who adds 1 baby every day.

a) How many total bugs do I have after one day? After 3 days? After 5 days? After 10 days? (Assume the babies cannot reproduce.)

b) Create a scatter plot relating the number of days to the number of bugs. Draw the line of best fit and write the equation of the line.

c) Use your line to predict after what day I will have 50 bugs.

Think Beyond

11. You can find a line of best fit on your graphing calculator. This is called a regression line. Find out how to do this and plot the regression line for the temperature data in Question 3 on your calculator. Was your line from Question 3 close to the one you found with your calculator? Do they both have the same or close to the same *y*-intercept? Do they both have the same or close to the same slope?

 Think Back

To make the most of her heaping pile of gold, Erica decided to invest in the stock of one of four companies: Grislaw Food Co., R&K Discount Novels, Magnificent Marbles Industries and Medieval Lettering Company. She began tracking their progress over a week, and charted their rates. The data are presented below:

Magnificent Marbles Industries

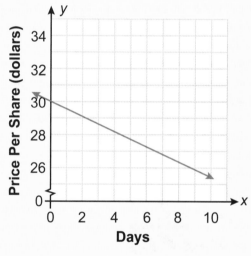

R&K Discount Novels

Grislaw Food Company

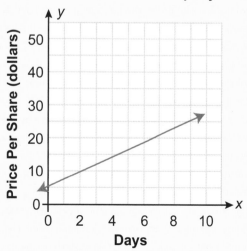

Medieval Lettering Company

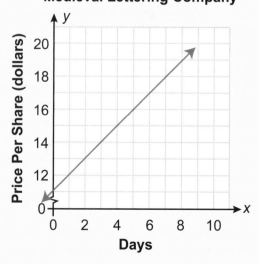

12. Which stock increased the most over the course of the first seven days? By how much did it increase?

13. Which stock had the highest price at the end of the seven-day period?

14. If Erica has $200 dollars, which company should she invest in? Assume that she is buying the stock on day seven, and that the stock continues to increase or decrease at its current rate. (Only a whole number of stock shares may be purchased or sold.)

15. How much money would she have if she sold the stock purchased in Question 14 on day 10? (Only a whole number of stocks may be purchased or sold).

16. Erica is worried about having all her money in one stock, so she decides to put $60 into each of the three stocks that are going up in value. If she puts this money in on day 7 and sells all the stocks on day 10, how much money will she have? (Only a whole number of stocks may be purchased.)

Optional Technology Lesson
for this section available
in your eBook

Sum It Up

In this section you examined data to see if there was a relationship between the variables. If a relationship exists, a line of best fit can be drawn to help tell the story about the data and also to show patterns that allow you to predict other data points that were not in the original set. The important mathematical ideas in this section include the following:

Correlation: Two variables that are related in some way are said to have a correlation between them.

- In a **positive correlation,** there is a general trend such that as one variable increases, the other tends to increase.

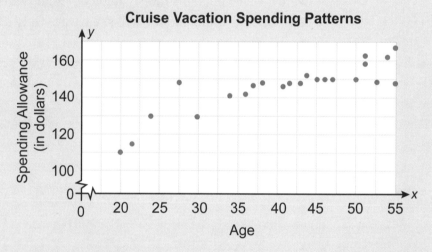

- In a **negative correlation,** there is a general trend such that as one variable increases, the other tends to decrease.

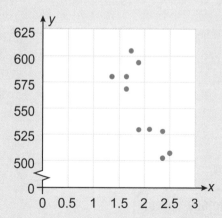

- A **perfect correlation** means the two variables are related in exactly the same manner in every ordered pair. The graph below shows a perfect correlation. Notice that it is a straight line. In fact, it is a linear function.

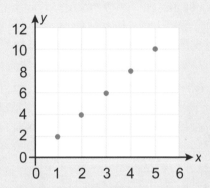

- Sometimes there is **no correlation** between variables, and this is shown graphically by the data points being scattered in such a way that no trend or pattern can be determined.

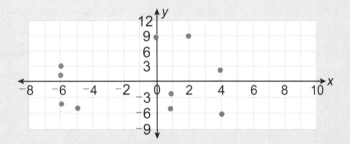

Line of Best Fit

- A **line of best fit** is a line drawn on a scatter plot to help show trends in the data. Approximately half the points on the scatter plot should fall above this line and half should fall below this line.

In this section, you learned about three different ways to create a line of best fit:

- The "**spaghetti method**" uses a thin strand of spaghetti to approximate a line where half the points are above and half are below.

- Another method uses the **mean** of the values graphed on the *x*-axis and the mean of the values graphed on the *y*-axis to create a new data point (mean of *x*-values, mean of *y*-values). A line of best fit is drawn through the mean with about half the data values above the mean and half below the mean.

■ A third method uses **box-and-whisker** plots. Box-and-whisker plots are created for the data on the *x*-axis and the data on the *y*-axis. A box is formed on the scatter plot with the data points whose four vertices are comprised of the Q1 and Q3 values of each box-and-whisker plot. These four vertices are called **Q-points**. The diagonal of the box is the line of best fit.

Hours Teens Talk with a Friend Compared to Math Test Scores

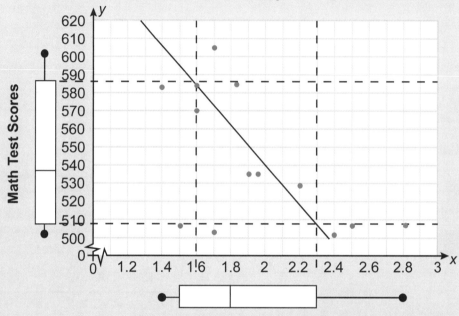

Time in Hours Teens Talk with a Friend

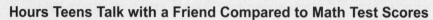

Part 1. What did you learn?

1. Match each term with the correct description.

a.	positive correlation	**f.**	Two variables are related in exactly the same manner for every ordered pair in the data set.
b.	negative correlation	**g.**	A general trend exists between two variables such that as one variable increases, the other increases.
c.	perfect correlation	**h.**	Helps analyze trends in the data. Approximately half the point on the scatter plot should fall above and below it.
d.	no correlation	**i.**	A general trend exists between two variables such that as one variable increases, the other decreases.
e.	line of best fit	**j.**	Two variables are not related to each other in any predictable way.

2. State whether each scatter plot implies a positive, negative or no correlation.

a.

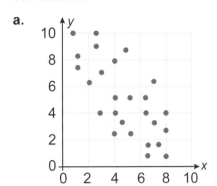

b.

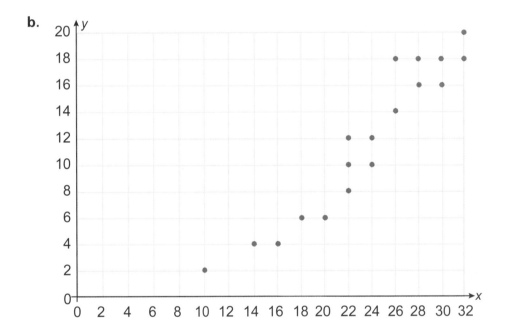

c.

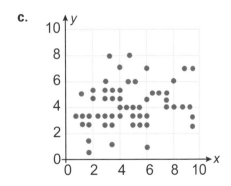

3. Each player on the basketball team kept track of her number of practice shots made and the number of shots missed. They graphed their data in the scatter plot below and drew a line of best fit.

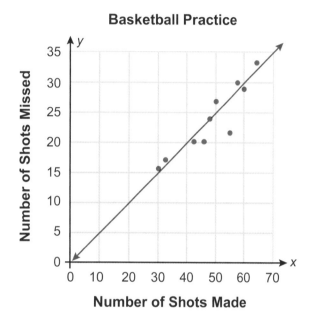

Basketball Practice

a. Determine whether each of the following equations is reasonable or not reasonable for the line of best fit. Explain your reasoning.

I. $y = x$

II. $y = 0.5$

III. $y = 0.5x$

b. How many students made at least 40 shots?

c. How many students missed at most 25 shots?

d. What is true about the points below the line of best fit in this situation?

e. What is true about the points above the line of best fit in this situation?

4. Nathaniel looked for a correlation between the number of songs on an MP3 player and the number of minutes its owner spends listening to music each day. He collected data from 17 friends.

Number of Songs	Number of Minutes Spent Listening to Music (rounded to the nearest 5 minutes)
10	10
12	15
14	5
15	10
15	15
20	15
22	20
25	20
27	25
30	25
30	30
32	30
32	10
34	25
34	40
35	30
38	32

a. Draw a scatter plot of the two data. Plot the number of songs on the *x*-axis and the number of minutes on the *y*-axis.

b. Use the mean of each value to draw a line of best fit.

   1. Find the mean of the values graphed on the *x*-axis.

   2. Find the mean of the value graphed on the *y*-axis.

   3. Use these values to create a new data point.

   4. Draw a line through this point so that half of the data values are above the mean and half are below.

c. What does the scatter plot and the line of best fit tell you about the relationship between number of songs on a person's MP3 player and the number of minutes they spend listening to music? Explain.

5. Zelda and Brindley looked at the scatter plot below.

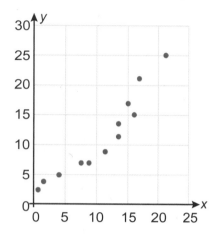

Zelda said, "As the *x*-values go up, the *y*-values go up too."
Brindley responded, "Yes, so that means there is a perfect
correlation between the variables." What is wrong with
Brindley's reasoning?

Unit Study Guide

Part 1: What did you learn?

SECTION 1

1. Match each term with the correct definition.

a.	mean	i.	The difference between the minimum and maximum values in a data set
b.	median	ii.	The distribution of fair shares among the values of the data set or the balance point in the data set.
c.	mode	iii.	The middle value of an ordered data set.
d.	range	iv.	The most frequent value in the data set.

2. Create a set of data that satisfies the following criteria:

   • There are exactly six pieces of data.

   • The range of the data is 12.

   • The mean of the data is 8.

   • The median of the data is greater than the mean.

3. Create a data set of six whole numbers with a median of 4.5.

4. Find the mean of each of the following data sets using the equal shares method.

   a. 3.5, 2, 5.5, 4, 1

   b. 110, 90, 85, 100, 80

   c. 4, 4, 4, 0

   d. −4, 0, 4, 8, 12

5. Find the median of each of the data sets from Question 4.

6. Can the mean value of a data set ever be the same as the minimum value of that data set? Why or why not?

7. The data set below shows the numbers of e-mails students in Mrs. Kilban's class receive each day. The mean number of e-mails received is 4.

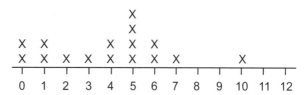

Number of e-Mails Received Each Day

a. Explain how the values balance around the mean.

b. What is the median value in the data set?

c. What is the range of values in the data set?

d. What is the mode of the data set?

SECTION 2

8. Match the description with the name of the data display.

a.	circle graph	**i.**	used with data grouped in numerical intervals
b.	bar graph	**ii.**	gives a five-number summary of the data
c.	line plot	**iii.**	used to show percentages or parts of a single whole
d.	histogram	**iv.**	usually used to organize large sets of data from least to greatest
e.	stem-and-leaf plot	**v.**	used to showed actual numbers of given categories
f.	box-and-whisker plot	**vi.**	used to show actual numbers of given categories of a small data set

9. Identify one type of graph that would *not* be appropriate for each set of data described below. Give at least one reason for each of your choices.

a. Number of U.S. presidents your classmates can name in one minute

b. Number of pets your classmates own

c. Favorite type of music of each of your classmates

10. The box-and-whisker plot shows data about the number of times the students in Mrs. Kilban's class accessed the Internet in one week.

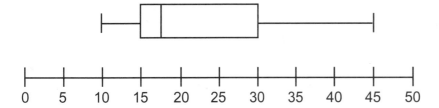

a. What is the range of the data?

b. Why is one whisker longer than the other?

c. What is the median value of the data?

d. Are the scores in the box evenly distributed about the median? Why or why not?

11. The students in Mr. Kendall's class responded to the following survey question: How many hours each week do you play a video game? The data are plotted on the box-and-whisker plot below.

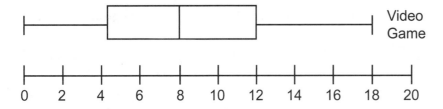

The students were also asked this question: How many hours each week do you play a sport or exercise? The data collected were 4, 5, 5, 5, 8, 8, 9, 10, 10, 10, 12, 12, 12, 12, 13, 14, 14 and 14.

a. Copy the box-and-whisker plot above.

b. Make a box-and-whisker plot for the sport/exercise data set. Plot your box-and-whisker plot above the box-and-whisker plot showing the video game data.

c. Use your two box-and-whisker plots to compare and contrast the video game and sports data. Write at least three statements.

12. For each pair of scatter plots below, determine which choice (i or ii) is the better representation of the line of best fit. Justify each choice.

Pair a

i.

ii.

Pair b

i.

ii.

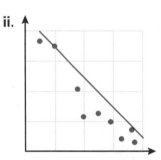

13. Determine whether each situation implies a positive correlation, negative correlation or no correlation between the two variables listed.

	Situation
a.	Number of inches of snow and number of tickets sold at a ski resort
b.	Fielding errors and number of starts for a first baseman on a baseball team
c.	A person's height and hair length
d.	Side length of a square and perimeter of the square

14. Determine whether each graph shows a positive, negative or no correlation.

a.

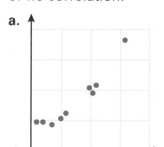

c.

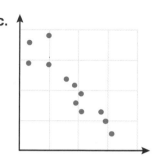

b.

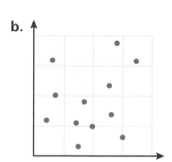

d.

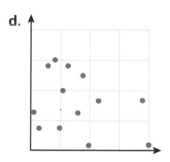

15. The students in Mrs. Kilban's class (from Question 7) also kept track of how many e-mails they sent each day. Here are the data for number of e-mails sent and number of e-mails received in one day.

No. of E-Mails Sent	2	0	0	3	4	4	3	7	5	6	5	6	6	7	6	4
No. of E-Mails Received	0	0	1	4	10	2	1	4	6	5	5	5	7	6	5	3

a. Plot the data points on a scatter plot. Plot number of e-mails sent on the *x*-axis and number of e-mails received on the *y*-axis.

b. Find the point (mean number of e-mails sent, mean number of e-mails received). Draw the line of best fit using this point.

c. Find the five-number summary of the data set for the number of e-mails sent.

d. Are there any outliers in the data set for the number of e-mails sent? Why or why not?

e. Copy the box-and-whisker plot of the number of e-mails received on your scatter plot.

f. Make a box-and-whisker plot of the number of e-mails sent. Plot your box-and-whisker plot below the *x*-axis.

g. Draw the line of best fit by using your box-and-whisker plots and the Q-points.

h. Compare the data about the number of e-mails sent and the number of e-mails received. What conclusions can you make?

Part 2. What went wrong?

16. Alice was asked to find the mean of the following set of data: 5, 5, 5, 0. She said, "That's easy; the mean is 5." What is wrong with Alice's reasoning? What could you say or do to help Alice find and fix her error?

17. Jerome looked at the box-and-whisker plot in Question 10 and said, "Something must be wrong here. The median divides a set of data in half. Half the data are below the median and half are above. So, why is the line showing the median not in the middle of the box?" What is wrong with Jerome's reasoning? What would you say or do to help Jerome?

bimodal set A set that has two modes.

Example:
The set {1, 4, 6, 6, 6, 8, 8, 9, 9, 9, 10, 10} is bimodal with modes of 6 and 9.

box-and-whisker plot (box plot) A diagram that summarizes a set of data using the median, the upper and lower quartiles, and the extreme values.

Example:
Box-and-whisker plot from data:
{53, 64, 76, 78, 79, 80, 83, 85, 86, 95, 98}

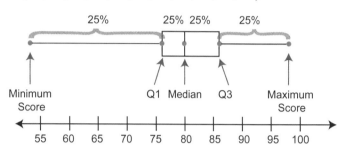

categorical data Data that can be categorized or grouped.

Example:
Birth month: January, February, March
Eye color: brown, blue, hazel, green
Grade Level: 7th grade, 8th grade, 9th grade

clusters A group of data points that lie within a small interval.

Example:
The set {1, 3, 4, 5, 6, 9, 10, 10, 20} has two clusters of data: {3, 4, 5, 6} and {9, 10, 10}.

correlation A relationship between two variables.

Example:
Correlated variables:

- miles driven and gasoline used
- minutes of exercise and calories burned
- years of ownership and value of a vehicle

data Facts or numbers that describe something such as people, places and things.

Example:
Pay per hour: $5.75, $10.00, $23.00, $55.15
Education level: 8th grade, high school, college
Population: 15 thousand, 3.75 million, 1 billion

data analysis The analysis or breaking down into parts of data for the purpose of gaining additional information, inferring patterns or trends and addressing questions related to the data.

descriptive statistics The basic facts and descriptors used to characterize a set of data.

Example:
mean, median, mode, range

deviation from the mean The distance of a data point from the mean value of a data set.

Example:
The set {1, 4, 5, 6, 8, 9, 9, 10, 11} has a mean of 7 and the deviation of the point 4 from the mean is 3.

distribution of data The spread of a data set as described by measures or descriptors.

Example:
The distribution of the set {1, 3, 4, 5, 6, 9, 10, 10, 20} is described by the following:
- range is 20 − 1 = 19
- clusters exist at {3, 4, 5, 6} and {9, 10, 10}
- gaps occur between 1 and 3, between 6 and 9 and between 10 and 20
- the point 20 appears to be an outlier

first or lower quartile, Q1 The median of the data values below the median of the entire data set.

Example:
The set {1, 4, 5, 6, 8, 9, 9, 10, 11} has a median of 8 and the Q1 value is 4.5, the median of the set {1, 4, 5, 6}.

five-number summary A summary description of a data set that includes the minimum value, Q1 value, median value, Q3 value and maximum value.

Example:
The five-number summary of the set {1, 4, 5, 6, 8, 9, 9, 10, 11} is:
Minimum = 1, Q1 = 4.5, Median = 8, Q3 = 9.5, Maximum = 11

gap An interval that includes no data points.

Example:
The set {1, 3, 4, 5, 6, 9, 10, 10, 20} has gaps between 1 and 3, between 6 and 9 and between 10 and 20.

histogram A graphical presentation of numerical data displayed in intervals on one axis and the frequency of observations within those intervals on the other axis.

Example:

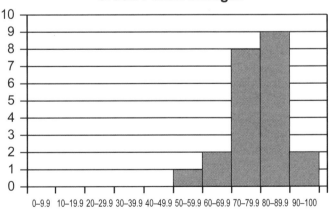

interquartile range The distance between the Q1 value and Q3 value of a data set.

Example:
The set {1, 4, 5, 6, 8, 9, 9, 10, 11} has a median of 8, a Q1 value of 4.5 and a Q3 value of 9.5. The interquartile range is 9.5 − 4.5 = 5.

line of best fit A line drawn on a scatter plot that best represents the relationship of the two variables.

Example:
The line of best fit for the relationship of y (estimated height) to x (actual height) is shown as the line $y = x$.

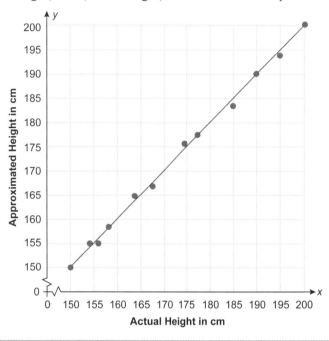

line plot A graph showing the frequency of values in a data set along a number line usually using an X to indicate data points. Line plots are used to graph small sets of data.

Example:
Set C: {1, 2, 6, 4, 2, 3, 2, 4}

The line plot for Set C is:

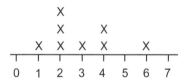

mean The arithmetic average of a set of numbers.

Example:
The mean of {4, 8, 2, 10, 15} is
$$\frac{4 + 8 + 2 + 10 + 15}{5} = 7.8.$$

measures of center (or of central tendency) Numerical values used to describe the overall "average" of a data set.

Example:
The most common measures of center are the mean, median and mode.

median The middle data value when the data points are arranged in order. If a data set has an even number of values, the median is the mean of the two middle values.

Example:
The median of {2, 4, 8, 10, 15} is 8.
The median of {5, 5, 8, 14, 20, 21} is $\frac{8 + 14}{2} = 11.$

mode The most frequent value in a data set.

Example:

The mode of {5, 5, 8, 14, 20, 21} is 5.

The set {3, 3, 3, 5, 6, 7, 7, 7, 9} is bimodal and has modes of 3 and 7.

The set {2, 4, 8, 10, 15} has no mode.

negative correlation A relationship between two variables such that as one variable increases the other variable decreases.

Example:

Negatively correlated variables:

  • miles driven and fuel remaining in tank

  • time since removing a casserole from the oven and the temperature of the casserole

Graphical Example:

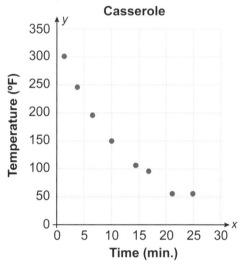

numerical data Data representing a quantity or quality that can be measured or counted.

Example:

Height: 38", 48", 56", 65"

Age: 11, 13, 21, 35, 54

Number of family members: 2, 4, 5, 7

outlier A data value that is much larger or much smaller than other values in the data set. More formally, a data point with a value that is 1.5 times the interquartile range ($1.5 \cdot (Q3 - Q1)$) larger than Q3 or smaller than Q1.

Example:

The set {1, 3, 4, 5, 6, 9, 10, 10, 20} has a Q1 value of 3.5 and a Q3 value of 10.

The interquartile range is $10 - 3.5 = 6.5$.

Since $1.5 \cdot 6.5 = 9.75$, outliers would be less than $3.5 - 9.75 = -6.25$ or greater than $10 + 9.75 = 19.75$.

Therefore. the data point 20 is an outlier.

perfect correlation A relationship between two variables such that they relate to each other in exactly the same way for every pair of data points.

Example:
Perfectly correlated variables:
- weight in pounds and weight in kilograms
- temperature in °C and temperature in °F

Graphical Example:

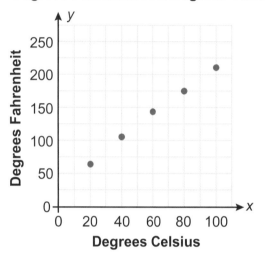

Degrees Fahrenheit vs. Degrees Celsius

positive correlation A relationship between two variables such that as one variable increases the other variable increases.

Example:
Positively correlated variables:
- miles driven and gasoline used
- minutes of exercise and calories burned

Graphical Example:

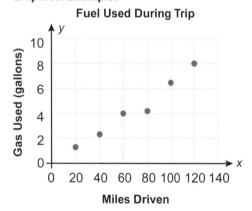

Fuel Used During Trip

Q-points The greatest value in each quartile of a data set.

Example:
Q1 is the greatest value of the first quartile, Q2 is the greatest value of the second quartile (also the median of the data set) and Q3 is the greatest value of the third quartile.

range The difference between the maximum value and the minimum value in the data set.

Example:
The set $\{1, 3, 4, 5, 6, 9, 10, 10, 20\}$ has a range of $20 - 1 = 19$.

scatter plot The graph of points representing sets of ordered pairs on a coordinate plane.

Example:

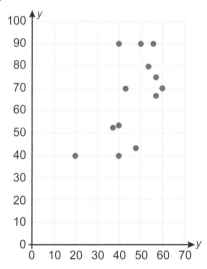

statistics A branch of mathematics that deals with the collection, organization, analysis and interpretation of numerical data.

stem-and-leaf plot A display of a data set organized in rows to show distribution by separating the last digits (leaves) from the previous digits (stem).

Example:
Data set $\{72, 76, 78, 79, 81, 86, 88, 88, 95, 98\}$:

7	2	6	8	9
8	1	6	8	8
9	5	8		

Key: 7 | 2 represents 72.

Data set $\{123, 125, 128, 134, 157, 159\}$:

12	3	5	8
13	4		
15	7	9	

Key: 12 | 3 represents 123.

third or upper quartile, Q3 The median of the data values above the median of the entire set.

Example:
The set $\{1, 4, 5, 6, 8, 9, 9, 10, 11\}$ has a median of 8 and the Q3 value is 9.5, the median of the set $\{9, 9, 10, 11\}$.

Lesson 1.1

A Balancing Act

Page 3, Question 7: The definitions of *mean* and *median* can be found in your glossary.

Lesson 1.2

The Perfect Balance

Page 14, Question 10b: You may want to put the numbers on a number line and use the mean as the balance point as in Part a.

Page 14, Question 12b: You can put the numbers on a number line and use the mean as the balance point, as in Part a.

Lesson 2.2

On Your Own

Page 59, Question 15: Use your graphing calculator.

Lesson 3.1

On the Go . . . Planning a Trip

Page 75, Question 9: Remember correlation does not by itself mean that the change in one variable is necessarily *causing* the change in the other variable. Think of other factors that could influence attendance.

On Your Own

Page 78, Question 1b: Consider the number of variables in the different types of data we are analyzing.

Lesson 3.2

On Your Own

Page 88, Question 7: A line of best fit is used to describe a relationship between two variables. Evaluate whether there is a relationship between these variables.

Index

A

assigned number values   (See *numerical data*.)

B

bar graphs   61. (See also *displays, graphs*.)
   vs. circle graphs   38
bimodal   3, 29, 115. (See also *measures of center*.)
box-and-whisker plot (box plot)   47–50, 53, 63, 115. (See also *displays*.)
   graphing calculator and   54
   to find line of best fit   93

C

categorical data   36, 61, 115. (See also *data, graphs*.)
   mean and median with   36
circle graphs   39, 61. (See also *displays, graphs*.)
clusters   3, 28, 115. (See also *clusters, distribution of data*.)
   in line plots   62
coordinate axes   69
   line $y = x$ as benchmark   83
   scatter plot on   71
correlation (between variables)   71, 77, 78, 100, 115
   cause and   79
   negative   73, 118
   perfect   101, 119
   positive   71, 119
   predicting   74

D

data   1, 115. (See also *categorical data, mean, median, mode, numerical data, range*.)
   analysis   1, 48 (using stem-and-leaf), 115
   coordinate axes to graph   69
   datum (sing.)   2
   distribution of   3
   five-number summary   48
   graphing calculator and   53
   interquartile range to identify outliers   51
   line of best fit   83, 85
   line plot to arrange   2
   outliers   51

range   2
   statistics to analyze   1
descriptive statistics   1, 115. (See also *statistics*.)
deviation from mean   116
displays, choosing and comparing   38, 40, 44, 49. (See also *bar graph, box-and-whisker plot, circle graph, histograms, stem-and-leaf, line plot, table*.)
distribution of data   3, 28, 116. (See also *data*.)
   minimum   28

F

first quartile, Q1 (or lower quartile)   48, 116. (See also *five-number summary, median*.)
five-number summary   48, 63, 116. (See also *data*.)

G

gaps   3, 28. (See also *clusters, distribution of data*.)
   in line plots   62
graphing calculator   52
   box-and-whisker plot on   54
   regression line   98
graphs   35, 39. (See also *displays, graphing calculator, histograms*.)
   bar vs. circle   38
   histogram   39, 40, 62
   Q points   94
   scatter plot   71

H

histogram   39, 40, 62, 116. (See also *displays, graphs*.)

I

interquartile range, to identify outliers   51, 63, 116. (See also *data, outliers*.)

L

linear function (perfect correlation)   101. (See also *correlation, variables*.)
line of best fit   83, 101, 117
   box-and-whisker to find   93, 102
   finding   92
   mean to find   101
   regression line as   98